AMERICAN PSYCHOLOGY SERIES

HENRY E. GARRETT, GENERAL EDITOR

PSYCHOLOGICAL DIAGNOSIS IN SOCIAL ADJUSTMENT
By PERCIVAL M. SYMONDS

THE PSYCHOLOGY OF THE AUDIENCE
By H. L. HOLLINGWORTH

PSYCHOLOGICAL FOUNDATIONS OF EDUCATION
By J. STANLEY GRAY

FEELING AND EMOTION: A HISTORY OF THEORIES
By H. M. GARDINER
RUTH CLARK METCALF
and
JOHN G. BEEBE-CENTER

THE ORGANISM
By KURT GOLDSTEIN

MENTAL HYGIENE: A MANUAL FOR TEACHERS
By J. D. M. GRIFFIN
S. R. LAYCOCK
and
W. LINE

THE PRACTICE OF CLINICAL PSYCHOLOGY
By STANLEY D. PORTEUS

MENTAL HYGIENE

A MANUAL FOR TEACHERS

By

J. D. M. GRIFFIN, M.D.
Associate Medical Director
The National Committee for Mental Hygiene (Canada)

S. R. LAYCOCK, Ph.D.
Professor of Educational Psychology
College of Education, University of Saskatchewan

and

W. LINE, Ph.D.
Associate Professor of Psychology
University of Toronto

AMERICAN BOOK COMPANY

New York   Cincinnati   Chicago
Boston   Atlanta   Dallas   San Francisco

TO

SIR EDWARD BEATTY, G.B.E., K.C., D.C.L., LL.D.

A GREAT CANADIAN

FOREWORD

It is becoming increasingly obvious that mental hygiene and education are related disciplines, with great possibilities for significant contributions to human welfare through collaborative efforts. In so far as education must take into account what might be termed the human element—the intrinsic nature of those who are to be taught, and their vital needs in the way of intellectual, emotional, and social development—in respect to such considerations, mental hygiene offers a great storehouse of rich experience. And, turning to mental hygiene with its aim of conserving mental health, it is evident that most can be achieved through the processes of education.

This partnership between education and mental hygiene is being stimulated by a growing conviction that many personal and social ills that beset our present-day civilization could have been prevented by more enlightened and understanding arrangements in our schools and homes. We are no longer content to combat mental illness, crime, and a host of lesser evils through attention to end products alone. With our increasing knowledge, we are satisfied that much can be done in a preventive way through the sound education of youth that involves a clinical as well as a pedagogic approach. And, from our experience to date in the integration of mental hygiene with education, we discover that we can not only make gains in prevention, but we can also enrich education on the cultural side for children generally.

It should be stressed that anything falling short of actual partnership between education and mental hygiene will not be enough. The placing of psychiatrists and psychologists in our schools for the testing of children and for the guidance of so-called difficult cases is a valuable procedure, but does not constitute the full integration that is necessary. There is needed the active participation of supervisors, principals, and teachers, and, indeed, of parents, in setting the stage and creating a favorable environment for wholesome child development. In other words, teachers and parents themselves must be mental hygienists as well as educators.

With the aim of fostering this union between mental hygiene and education, three Canadians have collaborated in the writing of this Manual. They have approached their task from the angles of psychiatry, psychology, and education. They have all participated in classroom activities, and their perspective is from the standpoint of the teacher. Not only are they fully conscious of the splendid possibilities for constructive school efforts, but they are also sensitive to the many difficulties that confront the overworked teaching profession.

For several years the coauthors have been engaged in a study of shy children in Toronto, Saskatoon, and Montreal. This work, financed by the Supreme Council, 33° Scottish Rite Masons, Northern Jurisdiction, U. S. A., furnished the opportunity for the collection of a considerable amount of material that appears in this volume, and it is fitting to make acknowledgment to this great philanthropic body.

In presenting this Manual to teachers in the United States and Canada, it is realized that it offers merely an introduction to the subject of mental hygiene as it relates to education. Work in this field has only commenced. Genuine large-scale achievements remain as prospects for the future. The authors, who are my colleagues in the work of the National Committee for Mental Hygiene in Canada feel that if this Manual serves as a stimulus to progress, their modest efforts will not have been in vain.

CLARENCE M. HINCKS

General Director
National Committee for Mental Hygiene, Canada
Formerly General Director
National Committee for Mental Hygiene, United States

CONTENTS

CHAPTER I

MENTAL HEALTH—A CHALLENGE TO EDUCATION

I. SURVEYING THE PRODUCTS OF OUR SCHOOLS

Twenty years ago over two million children entered the elementary schools of the United States and Canada for the first time. What has happened to them?

The question is easily asked, but not easily answered. Our information is bound to be fragmentary; our answers, partial.

We know that, although many of these children went on to high school, less than 5% were graduated from our universities. The rest left school at various ages and for various reasons—ill-health, economic difficulties, domestic responsibilities, lack of ability, lack of interest in schoolwork. . . .

We know that their present occupational status varies considerably. Some are now members of the professional group; others are engaged in industry and farming; still others practice skilled crafts or belong to the group popularly known as "unskilled laborers"; and so on. A considerable proportion (10 to 15%) are unemployed, and the majority of these and their dependents are on relief. Some have never experienced the satisfaction of constructive employment.

Similar variation would be found were we to conduct the survey along other lines. Financial and economic status, criminal record, health, participation in social affairs, civic status, political leadership, church membership, contributions to scientific research—a perplexing and lengthy list of possible outcomes complicates our task indefinitely.

If we seek, not to survey the present circumstances of the school children of twenty years ago, but to prophesy the condition and character of today's generation twenty years from now, our task is still more difficult. The rapid changes, so characteristic of modern life, make prediction, even in one particular line, little more than a fair guess.

II. IS THE SCHOOL INTERESTED IN THE PRODUCTS?

Confronted with the complexity of the problem of surveying the products of our schools and of predicting the possible outcomes of education, we, as teachers, may do one of two things. We may profess indifference to outcomes, content ourselves with teaching a prescribed subject matter, and leave to government officials the problem of the real function of the school; or we may constantly keep in mind the future of our children, assume the school's effectiveness in determining character, and affirm a primary interest in the human products of education.

A description of desirable products may be found in most statements of educational creed. In the General Report of the "Regents' Inquiry into the Character and Cost of Public Education in the State of New York" [1] there occurs the following statement:

"Above all else, New York wants its schools to build character. It wants the rising generation to be honest, generous, courageous, friendly, and considerate, to believe in and have the habit of working hard, and to be accurate and responsible. We, in this State, want youth to learn how to work with others

[1] *Education for American Life.* McGraw-Hill Book Company, New York, 1938, page 39.

toward these same ends, to be tolerant of others' opinions, sensitive to their needs and suffering, and prepared to act intelligently and unselfishly for the good of others. We want youth to believe in democracy and to know how to act in a system of society in which the common man participates in determining the course of events, not through physical force, but through free discussion, compromise, the rule of law, the loyal acceptance of group decisions, and the exercise of the continuous right and duty of free criticism. We want youth to find and give happiness in the intimate relationships of life, to be cheerful but not inactive in adversity, temperate and healthful in life, inventive in disposition, and increasingly capable of finding rational solutions to problems as they arise. We want the rising generation to grow up into men and women who, of their own volition, will budget their time and their lives intelligently and effectively between their work, their rest, their recreation, their growth, their intimate friends and family, their civic responsibilities, their artistic interests, and their spiritual life."

"Above all else." The words are not idle. The school's interest in outcomes is centered in the personalities of pupils and the development of their character. So the school persists in assuming an effect that it cannot prove, in hoping for results that it cannot predict.

While it is not the sole agency obligated to consider the problems of personality development, the school has accepted the challenge that these problems involve.

III. THE NATURE AND THE POINT OF VIEW OF THIS MANUAL

In this Manual there is no attempt to discuss the problems of outcomes in relation to the many points of view from which society may regard the products of the school. The child, whatever the nature of his parentage, his intellectual or physical equipment, his economic and social background, and in whatever social group he may ultimately be centered, is always faced with the necessity of living with himself and with others. These two aspects involve opportunities and responsibilities. Can we direct the child's educational experience in such a way that he will make the most of his opportunities, enjoy his leisure and social living? Is he going to be not only well skilled, but also well directed in the use of his mental and physical equipment? Will he be fearful, timid, overanxious, seclusive, insecure, chaotic, or will he enjoy a rich emotional experience and a satisfying life of progressive achievement?

These are problems in mental health; to such problems, in their relationship to the classroom, this book confines itself.

IV. THE IMPORTANCE OF MENTAL HEALTH

Mental hygiene is only one facet of education. But of the many angles from which educational responsibility may be regarded, none is more significant than that which points to facts about the mental well-being of the individual.

Consider, for example, the "outcomes" of one hundred elementary-school children selected at random, without regard to age, sex, or grade. The following predictions may be made if the trends of the last twenty years are maintained:

Four or five will spend part of their lives in mental hospitals.

Four or five more will develop serious mental illnesses, which will be cared for at home or in institutions other than mental hospitals.

One or two will commit some major crime or delinquency and will spend some part of their lives in jails or penitentiaries.

Three or four will be so handicapped by retarded or stunted mental development that, without special training or other provision, they will have difficulty in becoming useful and productive citizens.

Of the remainder, it is estimated that from thirty to fifty will fail to reach the maximum efficiency and happiness in life possible for them, because of unwholesome emotional habits and personality traits.

A teacher of an average class of forty children may thus expect that in later life seventeen to twenty-six of her pupils will suffer from conditions ranging from unhappiness and a sense of futility to criminal behavior and insanity. Can education help to reduce this toll of mental ill-health? Observation suggests that education, while it may not be a panacea, can be a potent cure.

In a recent survey of two hundred cases examined and treated at a children's mental-hygiene clinic,[2] 166 children were judged to be suffering in their development because of inadequate training procedures in home or school. In 100% of the cases, the recommendations of the clinic referred to enriched educational facilities.

V. THE JOINT RESPONSIBILITY OF HOME AND SCHOOL

Many cases of human maladjustment and warped personality may be traced to factors over which the school has no control whatever. Heredity and inborn constitution may play a considerable part in some instances; economic difficulties, with their attendant ills, such as malnutrition, inadequate and unfortunate environmental circumstances, are influences that cannot be denied. Yet a great many instances of mental ill-health can be traced

[2] The Clinic for Psychological Medicine, Hospital for Sick Children, Toronto, Canada.

MH-2

directly to influences originating in the home and the school. It is with these two great social mechanisms for training healthy personalities that we are here concerned. To attempt to separate the school's responsibility from that of the home would be unwise, and, indeed, would set an impossible task. The safest procedure is to stress the joint responsibility these basic institutions have.

In most communities this partnership has not yet been adequately demonstrated. The home, in turning over its children to the school for purposes of some aspects of training, has tended to isolate itself from these aspects. The school is "employed" for the purpose of teaching the child to read, write, and compute, and to furnish the young mind with a body of factual knowledge that will be useful in later years. Without much thought concerning the intimate personal welfare of the child, the home has regarded the school as a highly specialized institution of knowledge where training may be obtained in the skills and prerequisites of social participation and vocational security. The school, in its turn, has regarded its function as different from that of the home. Yet when things go wrong, when the child fails to learn, to pay attention, to show adequate respect for the school, the teachers blame the home "for failing to nourish the child, to instill into the child's mind a respect for scholastic learning." If the child fails to show that personal development expected and desired by the home, the parents often blame the school. "The curriculum is not well designed." "Extracurricular activities are not suitable." "Teachers and administrators are not sufficiently sensitive to the needs of the individual children."

Concerning spheres of responsibility, the only sane attitude is one that regards ultimate success in child training as involving intimate partnership between home and school. The problem of the school is to fulfill its obligations in that partnership; so, also, the problem of the home. Though the greater part of this Manual is addressed to teachers, it assumes, throughout, the partnership of home and school, and the obligations of each.

VI. PROBLEMS OF MENTAL HYGIENE IN THE CLASSROOM

The obligations of the school deal mainly with the following problems:

(*a*) What are the aspects of child development that are related to the school's task of fostering mental health?

(*b*) What are the characteristics that can be observed in children, at different age levels, that imply healthy mental activity?

(*c*) What signs or symptoms of mental ill-health can be observed by the classroom teacher?

(*d*) How do these symptoms reflect possible needs of the child in his present and future adjustment, and what are the educational provisions that can be offered to assist the process of healthy development?

(*e*) How are the child's needs related to his mental equipment?

(*f*) What provisions can be made for special disabilities?

(*g*) How shall we conceive the role of the home in relation to that of the school, of the neighborhood, and so on?

(*h*) In what ways is the teacher's mental health important, not only to himself, but also to his pupils?

(*i*) How may the curriculum, extracurricular activities, factors in school organization and administration contribute to mental health?

Succeeding chapters of this book are concerned with a discussion of these questions.

CHAPTER II

THE NATURE OF DEVELOPMENT

I. GROWTH AND DEVELOPMENT

Growth or development is a characteristic of *life*. Development involves change or *process*. It is not a question of simple expansion, like blowing up a balloon. Nor is it a matter of addition, such as making a structure larger and more complicated by the adding of bricks. It is essentially a vital process of change coming "from within" and affecting the whole organism, both in structure and in function. The power or capacity to grow and develop is a characteristic which the organism receives from its antecedents. It is part of the native endowment with which it starts life. Emotional factors and conditions can influence development for better or worse, but they cannot stop it. External forces can mold, support, warp, or modify development, but, short of killing the organism, they cannot prevent development.

Growth and development can be observed and measured by selecting a unit of time as a point of reference. Thus, we can assume that the average growing child will achieve successively definite stages of maturity with successive months or years. This is the basis on which comparisons are made in all development, whether it is concerned with physical growth, intelligence, or personality. It must not be imagined from this that development takes place at the same rate in all individuals, or even that the rate remains constant for one individual. Each child has a pattern of development unique to him.

Even in the individual himself, certain organs, members, aspects of behavior may mature at apparently varying rates.

"When examined in detail, the developmental complex proves to be very intricate. In the very nature of things, individuality makes it impossible for all the components of behavior (postural, perceptual, adaptive, language, and social) to mature in lock step along an unbroken front. At any given moment the margin of advance is an irregular rather than a smooth line. Furthermore, over a long series of moments the margin shows fluctuations, possibly rhythmic in character. The tide of behavior development does not move erratically, but it moves unevenly. In vague analogy we may picture surface currents, undercurrents, apparent backflows, eddies, pools, in the ceaseless streaming of morphogenetic events, which we call mental growth." [1]

II. HOW PERSONALITY DEVELOPS

Our concern with mental hygiene leads us to consider particularly the development of personality. By personality, we mean *the sum total of the individual's characteristic habits, attitudes, and persistent tendencies*. Almost everything the child *does* or is *able to do* is a function of his personality, which, again, by definition, is reflected in his everyday behavior. Just as no two children behave exactly alike, so no two children have exactly the same personality. A healthy personality in a child, like a healthy body, is something that changes from year to year as development proceeds; and by observation of these changes at various levels of growth, it is possible to describe, in some measure, the progress of personality development.

[1] Arnold Gesell, *et al., Biographies of Child Development*, Paul B. Hoeber, Inc., New York, 1939.

A child five years of age, for instance, should show certain personality traits consistent with his development. He should have an active interest and curiosity concerning the world about him. He should have no excessive timidity or fears of the everyday objects and factors in his environment such as animals, storms, the dark, other children, or adults. He should generally be happy and cheerful and have his share of self-confidence. He should be able to make friends and play with other children, if necessary sharing his toys with them. He should not be too dependent on others and should be able to amuse himself when he has to be alone.

The normal child of ten has a personality which reflects certain changes. He is more mature in his habits and attitudes. He has learned to do his work promptly and to do the disagreeable tasks that fall to him without shirking or complaining. He has learned the value of being kind and thoughtful to others; and he has begun to appreciate some of the niceties of social living. He is willing to obey the rules of the group, but is quite capable of thinking things through for himself. And he has learned to express most of his thoughts in language, whether spoken or written. In other words, he shows the results of an increasing integration of experience; he is beginning to accept reality with equanimity, whether it is the inconvenient but natural reality of a thunderstorm or the equally inconvenient but somewhat artificial reality of mowing the lawn; he shows progressive ability to symbolize his ideas in terms of language; and he demonstrates conclusively that he has an ever-increasing power of self-direction.

III. NORMS OF HEALTHY PERSONALITY DEVELOPMENT [2]

So that the teacher can judge the approximate level of personality development in the children of his class, the following norms are here presented. This scale represents an ideal to be achieved, rather than the "average" personality of children at different ages.

A. Personality Characteristics of the Child Entering School

1. Shows a keen active interest and curiosity concerning the world about him.

2. Attends to whatever he is doing.

3. Completes his task successfully, reasonably often.

4. Is not excessively timid or afraid, for example, of animals, storms, the dark, and so forth.

5. Enjoys humorous situations.

6. Is generally happy and cheerful.

7. Tends to be truthful.

8. Has self-confidence.

9. Does not use baby talk.

10. Has a place for his own possessions and is learning to care for them.

11. Enjoys play.

12. Is friendly with other children.

13. Is not afraid of other children (or strange adults).

14. Is able to amuse himself and is not dependent on adults in play.

15. Is willing to share his possessions.

16. Is interested in making other people happy and is willing to help them.

17. Shows respect for those in authority.

18. Makes reasonable generalizations.

[2] These norms have been adapted from the norms in *Health Behavior,* by T. D. Wood and M. O. Lerrigo, Public School Publishing Company, Bloomington, Illinois, 1927.

19. Has established socially acceptable habits in relation to bodily functions (for example, eating, sleeping, elimination, cleanliness, and so on).

20. Is well co-ordinated in his motor activity (for example, walking, running, manipulation, and so forth).

B. *Personality Characteristics of the Child in Grade Three or Four*

In addition to the foregoing he:

1. Shows persistence in more difficult tasks.
2. Does his work promptly, without procrastinating.
3. Is learning not to shirk disagreeable duty.
4. Enjoys schoolwork and activities.
5. Meets disappointments bravely.
6. Remains good-humored under somewhat trying circumstances.
7. Controls himself in anger, fear, or other strong emotions.
8. Forgets grudges quickly.
9. Shows kindness to those who are weaker or younger; does not tease or bully.
10. Shows kindness towards animals.
11. Obeys the rules of the group; is willing to take part in group activities and assists in planning them.
12. Waits his turn.
13. Settles difficulties without appealing to the teacher.
14. Refrains from interrupting others needlessly.
15. Refrains from quarreling.
16. Gives back lost things to their owner, if possible.
17. Refrains from taking what belongs to other children.

C. *Personality Characteristics of the Child in Grade Six or Seven*

In addition to the above he:

1. Is curious concerning the world about him and seeks by experiment and observation to satisfy this curiosity.

2. Has a keen, active interest in either friends, sports, hobbies, or in all.

3. Meets difficulties squarely without dodging the issue.

4. Develops increasing initiative in work and play.

5. Develops orderly habits (work and play).

6. Assumes increasing responsibilities at home and school.

7. Refrains from brooding and worrying.

8. Shares his pleasures and possessions with others.

9. Respects the rights and property of others.

10. Co-operates with others in work or play.

11. Develops increasing independence, ability, and willingness to solve his own problems.

12. Is beginning to recognize the value of social and moral customs and tradition; for example, uses only suitable language, has wholesome relationships with opposite sex, takes part in social conversations without interrupting or monopolizing, and so forth.

13. Is trying to overcome any shyness or embarrassment in the presence of strangers or in social situations.

D. Personality Characteristics of the Child in Grade Nine or Ten

In addition to the above he:

1. Persists in his work, completing whatever task he commences.

2. Is honest, both with others and with himself.

3. Cultivates a habit of cheerful calm and poise.

4. Does not permit shyness or embarrassment to overcome him in the presence of other people, in carrying on either his social relationships or his work.

5. Cultivates a sense of humor and a sense of proportion.

6. Forgets grudges, jealousies, and suspicions quickly.

7. Takes adequate rest and exercise, and in other respects follows a hygienic regimen.

8. Avoids forming habits of hurry and excitement.

9. Knows that there is hygienic value in controlling his emotions.

10. Knows which emotions are wholesome.

11. Knows that boys and girls can control their own emotional habits.

12. Has an intelligent understanding of what his responsibilities are towards other persons.

13. Knows how to study.

14. Knows in what sources he may satisfy his curiosity about his environment: books, magazines, and so on.

15. Regards the prospects of future love, marriage, home-making, and parenthood as the natural, normal privilege of all young persons.

16. Has a wholesome ideal of normal friendly relationships between boys and girls.

17. Has a developing sense of responsibility for the well-being of friends, family, schoolmates, and community.

18. Chooses wholesome recreation.

IV. THE BASIS OF DEVELOPMENT

The age-old controversy between the relative influence of heredity and environment is still raging. About the only conclusion upon which all are agreed is the fact that *both* are important. On the one hand, in addition to his capacity for growth and development, there is little doubt that the child inherits certain potentialities from his parents and his ancestors. Whether or not his development will be limited by these potentialities depends, on the other hand, in great measure on the environmental conditions. For instance, a child may be born with a bodily constitution which is particularly susceptible to the influence of certain proteins. We say he has inherited his allergic tendencies from his antecedents. He *may* develop eczema, asthma, or hay fever; but again, he may not. If he is protected from a too-sudden introduction of the dangerous proteins, whether they be in food or in the atmosphere around him, he may never suffer from these annoying conditions. Similarly, a child may be born with the potentiality for great intelligence. If this intelligence is not carefully cultivated by allowing the child to develop in a stimulating environment, rich with the possibilities for new experience of all kinds, he may never be able to use his intelligence to the full. Several experimenters have recently adduced evidence to show that the intelligence quotients [3] of some children actually seem to rise when the children are placed in a good nursery school or a similar environment. Likewise the quotient occasionally falls when the children are allowed to grow up in the dull, colorless environment of the traditional orphan asylum.[4] Child psychology of the past has accustomed us to think of intelligence as fixed at birth, but these experiments, while inconclusive, may eventually lead us to modify this conception. Actually, they illustrate the fact that, while the capacity or upper limit of intelligence may be fixed at birth by factors beyond our control, the extent to which intelligence is used will depend very much on the environment and experience.

[3] The Intelligence Quotient (I.Q.) is now a familiar concept, used to designate a child's "general intelligence" as measured by a psychological examination of the Binet-Simon type. It will be discussed further in Chapters IV and V. At this point it is necessary only to remind teachers that the "normal" limits of intelligence have been arbitrarily set at I.Q. 90-110. Quotients below 90 tend to indicate "low," "dull," or "poor" intelligence; quotients above 110 tend to indicate "high" or "superior" intelligence.

[4] Wellman, B. L., "The Intelligence of Preschool Children, as Measured by the Merrill-Palmer Scale of Performance Tests," Iowa City, University of Iowa Studies; *Studies in Child Welfare,* Vol. XV, No. 3, 1930. Wellman's results are very striking, and an adequate interpretation of them has not yet been made. It may be that the intelligence tests used at the preschool level are themselves very susceptible to the influences of training. But in any case, the findings indicate wide differences between stimulating and nonstimulating environments.

Let us assume, then, that the child is born with certain potentialities and limitations. The nature and direction of his development from this point depend on the environment. But the story is not so simple as this. It is not merely a question of the environment influencing the child. The child also influences his environment. Allen had this fact in mind when he stated that:

"It is not enough to speak of the forces that enter this process [of development] as social or environmental. That carries a somewhat static connotation by viewing the child as a pawn, pulled here and there by forces that impinge upon him. I want to stress the more dynamic interplay between these forces and the emerging self of the child, a view that does not accept the child as a pawn but as a participant in his own growth. The child's behavior becomes the index of how this growth process is taking place." [5]

In other words, there is constant interplay between the child and the setting in which he finds himself. Both make demands on the other. The child has many fundamental needs which must be satisfied if development is to proceed in a normal, orderly fashion. The environment has many requirements which the child must meet in order that the environment, in turn, will be in a position to satisfy the child's needs. This sounds like argument in a circle, and perhaps it is. At least the argument assumes that there is a constant interplay and interaction of child and environment, and it is the nature of this interaction of forces which interests us at the moment. Some of these forces we may be able to control to affect the personality of the child.

[5] Allen, Frederick H., "Abnormal Behavior in Infancy and Childhood," Symposium on Mental Health, A.A.A.S., Winter Meeting, Richmond, Va., December 28, 1938.

V. THE CHILD'S NEEDS AS FACTORS IN DEVELOPMENT

Some psychologists regard the "needs" of the child as "appetites"; some as "drives" urging the child toward desired goals; some speak of them as the "wellsprings" of behavior, the "urges," the "instincts," the "fountains of life." Whatever simile may be used to describe their exact nature, they are certainly dynamic factors in personality development.

Children are sometimes quite conscious of the existence of their own needs, as when, for instance, they are hungry for food. More often, however, they are not aware of them; the child who is striving to satisfy his needs for self-assertion does not usually realize why he behaves as he does.

Briefly, there are three main types of needs: the *physiological*, the *social*, and the *self* (ego) needs.[6] The *physiological* (or somatic) needs are fundamental. In order to live and grow, the child, like all other animals, must be protected or able to protect himself from the common dangers. In addition to this primitive need for self-protection, there are the need for food and drink, the need for exercise, and the need for rest and sleep. So much is obvious. The metabolism and the biochemical balance of the body must be maintained at all cost.

Regularity of habits in connection with the satisfaction of these somatic needs is an important item in physical hygiene. Problems in eating, sleeping, and elimination occur very frequently in young children with whom the details of habit training have been carelessly managed. Although these seldom concern the school, teachers fre-

[6] These basic needs have been clearly outlined by Prescott in *Emotion and the Educative Process*, American Council on Education, Washington, D. C., 1938.

quently have to deal with problem behavior arising as a direct result of poor habit training. For instance, the child who has learned to obtain satisfaction from the emotional tension and dismay shown by his parents at his refusal to eat may find it difficult to adapt his behavior and personality to the school situation.

One important quality of these physiological needs is their cyclical character. The child is hungry, he eats, and he is satisfied. He is active, he plays and runs about, and then he rests. It is very important to remember these physiological rhythms in the classroom. Play and relaxation must follow work, rest must follow activity. Adults are fully aware of the value of a change in activity when they are losing interest or becoming physically tired.

The span of attention is generally shorter in children than in adults, and we can expect to find individual differences in rhythms among children. When a child is not "concentrating" as well as we think he should, boredom or fatigue may be the underlying factors. The proper balance between activity and rest is vital not only to the work habits and intellectual development of the child, but also to his personality development generally. Vigorous activity and play will help to dissipate emotional tensions, but lack of rest and sleep will tend to make the child fretful and irritable. Habit training once again plays an important role here. If the child is accustomed to stop his play at a regular time and begin a new form of activity, such as eating or sleeping in a quiet and restful environment, there will be little danger of his becoming overtired.

It is unfortunate that speed, noise, bustle, excitement, the spectacular, and the unusual characterize our modern life. Movies, radio, newspapers, and even some of our schools are reflecting this accelerated tempo of living. Existence is becoming too exciting and too thrilling, with the result that many of our children are being overstimulated. The consequent chronic fatigue is held by many physicians to be the greatest single cause of problems in children's personality development.

The *social* needs of the child are as simple to understand as his physiological needs. Essentially there are two kinds of emotional needs which can be satisfied only by the social milieu. The first is the need for personal love and affection. The child needs to feel that his parents—or someone—loves him for himself alone. He is to some extent appreciated because of *who* he is.[7] This affection gives him a deep and lasting sense of security.

The second is the need for acceptance and approval by the group, for appreciation by others because of *what* he is.[7] Sometimes this is in direct conflict with the first. The mother's love for her son, for instance, may be so possessive, powerful, and at the time, so completely satisfying to the child, that he does not feel the need for acceptance by the group. To this extent his personality development will be warped.

The need for social status and social approval shows itself constantly in children at school. Some children will go to great lengths to gain a cherished recognition. If they cannot achieve it by legitimate behavior, they sometimes try behavior that is unacceptable or even antisocial. The boy who wins the admiration of at least some of the class by his effrontery and rudeness to the teacher is doubtless in this category. The desire for status in the social group, and the sense of "belonging" which this

[7] See, for instance, the distinctions made by J. S. Plant in *Personality and the Cultural Pattern,* The Commonwealth Fund, New York, 1937.

brings, are powerful motives that are present in every-one.

The *self* (or ego) needs of the child can readily be appreciated by adults. We all need some self-respect. We all like to feel that we are worthy people, and that we are filling our place in the world in a satisfactory way. We are important because of what we can achieve and contribute. We want our fair share of success, and, in addition to any social satisfaction and increased status which success may bring to us, we get personal satisfaction from a job well done.

Most of us feel the need to assert ourselves a little now and then, to be dominant in certain situations, and so add to our self-respect. Equally important is our need for new experiences. The thrill of adventure, travel, or exploration, even when the exploring is limited to new fields of knowledge investigated for the first time in school or library, persists throughout life. If it does not, we are in danger of failing to achieve the fullest type of personality development. Of special interest to education are the natural demands for spontaneity, for creative expression, and for harmonious appreciation and integration of our various experiences.

The child experiences the same type of personal self-needs, and he should have all the opportunity possible to satisfy them.

Although most of these personality needs are present from an early age, the attempts which the child makes to satisfy them will vary with his development and will be modified by his growth and by his learning. The new-born baby suckles when he is hungry; the five-year-old has learned to use his knife and fork as a means to satisfy his appetite; the ten-year-old is learning a great deal about the necessity of manners and social amenities. Similarly, the egocentricity of the young child, his emphasis on the self-needs, become broadened later into the feeling of self-confidence and the achievement of individual satisfactions through co-operation with the group.

So far the emphasis has been placed on the urgency of satisfying all the interrelated personality needs of the child, without overemphasis or slighting of any one need. It will be obvious, however, that this satisfaction of the basic needs must be achieved with full consideration of the needs of other persons. Not till then will wholesome personality development take place. In other words, not only must the needs of the child be met by his environment, but the child must meet the requirements set by the people and institutions about him.

VI. THE SOCIAL REQUIREMENTS

From birth onward the child comes under the influence of an ever-increasing number of social institutions. At first there is only the family and the home, to whose rules and traditions he is expected to conform. Often it is difficult for the child to learn to obey the family rules, because they change so often, sometimes vigorously enforced, sometimes forgotten.

As his experience broadens, the child encounters some of the requirements of the neighborhood. He finds that while it may be all right to take an apple from his own cellar, it is distinctly wrong to take one from the house next door. Gradually the customs, taboos, and attitudes of his family and his neighbors become known to him. At first he learns them as "must nots"; then slowly some general principles evolve, and he builds up his system of codes and ethics. He may go to church and Sunday school, and there he may come into contact with a totally different set of rules and taboos. Occasionally these are in violent conflict with those he has learned to accept in his home and neighborhood.

By the time he starts to school, his environment has made many varied and complicated demands on him. The school adds more. Behavior must be adapted and the development of personality directed to meet these new demands and embrace wider responsibilities. The interplay of personality needs and social requirements is thus extremely complicated.[8] It is undoubtedly far more complicated than has been described so briefly here. Small wonder that in some children, for one reason or another, personality development becomes warped, retarded, or grotesque.

VII. DEVELOPMENT, GOOD AND BAD

We have assumed that wholesome personality will develop if the child, guaranteed good physical health, is able to satisfy his basic needs and meet his social requirements and responsibilities. Under these conditions growth and development of the individual potentialities are assured.

What happens if the child's basic needs cannot be adequately satisfied? What if the native equipment and inherited potentialities are not sufficient to meet the demands imposed by his environment? In this case, some sort of adjustment is attempted by the child. If some of his legitimate needs cannot be satisfied directly, he will attempt to balance things by overemphasizing other

[8] For the purpose of simplifying this chapter, an outline in diagrammatic form of the main dynamic factors affecting personality development is shown on page 23.

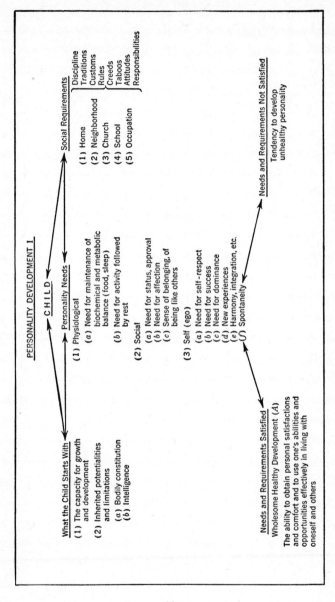

PERSONALITY DEVELOPMENT I

C H I L D

What the Child Starts With
(1) The capacity for growth
and development
(2) Inherited potentialities
and limitations
(a) Bodily constitution
(b) Intelligence

Personality Needs
(1) Physiological
  (a) Need for maintenance of
    biochemical and metabolic
    balance (food, sleep)
  (b) Need for activity followed
    by rest

(2) Social
  (a) Need for status, approval
  (b) Need for affection
  (c) Sense of belonging, of
    being like others

(3) Self (ego)
  (a) Need for self-respect
  (b) Need for success
  (c) Need for dominance
  (d) New experiences
  (e) Harmony, integration, etc.
  (f) Spontaneity

Social Requirements
(1) Home
(2) Neighborhood
(3) Church
(4) School
(5) Occupation

}
Discipline
Traditions
Customs
Rules
Creeds
Taboos
Attitudes
Responsibilities

Needs and Requirements Satisfied
Wholesome Healthy Development (A)
The ability to obtain personal satisfactions
and comfort and to use one's abilities and
opportunities effectively in living with
oneself and others

Needs and Requirements Not Satisfied
Tendency to develop
unhealthy personality

23

needs. If the needs are satisfied at the expense of *other* people's happiness and satisfactions, the social requirements will not be adequately met. In either case the developing personality is in danger. Sometimes the child, in his effort to satisfy his needs or meet his social requirements, behaves in a way which is unacceptable either from a social point of view or from the point of view of his own inner experience.

Whatever the situation, it must be remembered that personality development never stops. It may become perverted or stunted; it may take circuitous routes. But development goes on all the time. Perverted, warped, or circuitous personality development of the school child will be manifest by a wide variety of signs and symptoms. These range all the way from simple failure at school or excessive emotional behavior, to the more serious symptoms of malignant psychopathic personality.[9]

VIII. GROWTH THROUGH FAILURE

We hear a great deal nowadays about the necessity of avoiding failure; but, hypothetically at least, there is a place for it. If the child never experiences failure, he will never learn to overcome it. Some go so far as to claim that he will never learn anything if he fails at nothing. If failure is accepted in an objective way as a challenge— a challenge to succeed, to overcome the obstacle, to achieve the desired goal from which one is barred for the moment by the failure itself—then the failure is being used constructively and will actually contribute to sound, healthy development. For certain children, therefore, some failure is to be desired. Persistent failure, on the other hand, is dangerous. Other things being equal, the

[9] These will be discussed in some detail in the next chapter.

child should experience the satisfaction of successful achievement in schoolwork more often than he meets complete failure.

Supposing the child meets continued failure in the more abstract sense of failing to satisfy his basic personality needs; supposing the goal set by the child is obviously beyond his reach: is thwarted faulty development the inevitable result? From what has gone before, one might easily be led to believe that no other result can be expected. This is by no means the case. The signs and symptoms of poor personality development can be divided into two great classes—those representing an attempt on the part of the individual to *attack* the situation, and those representing his *withdrawal* from it.

Attacking Failure. There are many ways in which an individual may attack a situation in order that he may reduce to some sort of equilibrium the tensions set up by the lack of ability to satisfy his own needs or those of the environment. There is the emotional behavior of anger, with its various manifestations, temper tantrums, fighting, bullying, belligerence, and ordinary contentiousness. There are the various aggressive personality traits such as superiority, extreme egocentricity, the desire to dominate, and the tendency to exploit one's authority. Finally, there is the tendency for the individual to reject completely any set or traditional routine and to scoff at conventions. School failure for the child may occur here as a result of the manifestation of any of these tendencies.

The end result may be entirely destructive, leading to hopelessly inadequate personality development. The destructive outcome is usually in the form of minor or major delinquency and crime, rebellion against established law and order, tendencies toward violence, and cantankerous eccentricity. An entirely constructive outcome is possible, however. The tendency for attack can receive legitimate outlets in competitive sports and aggressiveness in business. Some individuals may direct this tendency into the field of social and political reform. In these ways the basic needs may be satisfied and wholesome development will be possible.

Withdrawing from Failure. But what of the reverse attitude? What of the individual who strives to reach a satisfactory equilibrium by withdrawing from his failures and inadequacies? There are many ways in which the individual can do this. Fear and fearful attitudes, such as anxiety, feelings of apprehension, and inferiority, leading to various forms of recessiveness, constitute one big group. Then there are various types of dependency, all of which represent a retreat from the situation. There is the extreme dependency on those in authority, for instance, as well as dependency on routine and convention. Extreme conservatism is thus a type of dependence.

Shrinking from accepting responsibility and various forms of social inadequacies are closely related to these. Rationalizing is a thinly disguised retreat from unpleasant realities, as are other forms of twisted thinking, including extreme suspiciousness and the tendency to blame other people for our own shortcomings. Failure of the child at school may be the indirect or direct result of some of these persistent tendencies.

The destructive outcome of persistent retreat from failure may take many forms. The various bad habits of the motor system, such as tics, stuttering, and others, are mildly disabling. Many individuals carry their retreat right into illness. Sometimes it leads to the so-called nervous breakdown, the minor or major forms of insanity, alcoholism, and drug addiction. The complete and final destructive outcome of such a persistent retreat is often suicide. On the bright side of the picture, however, there is much to be said. The end result need not be destructive. There are legitimate and healthy ways of utilizing the retreat tendency. The individual may become a scientific worker in research, or an artist, or a poet. There are hundreds of ways in which the shy, seclusive, or dependent person can utilize his assets without risking failure.[10]

Attacking Failure Intelligently. We have seen that both the attack and the withdrawal methods of reacting to failure can have healthy outcomes. Perhaps it is possible, from the first, to have a healthy development without the necessity for taking the circuitous route, with all the attendant symptoms. Let us assume that an individual is faced with a situation in which his desired goal is quite beyond him. What can he do to forestall the development of destructive personality results? A systematic attack on the problem will do much. He can analyze the problem in terms of the total situation, which includes a critical evaluation of himself, his assets, and liabilities. He may persist in his attempt to reach a satisfactory conclusion, trying first this procedure and then that. In all probability, however, he will quickly realize that the goal for the time being is too difficult for him. Once this decision is reached and accepted, a rational plan of procedure can be adopted. Energy and intelligence will then be conducted along other lines more conducive to successful achievement. The desired goal may be kept in mind, but deferred for a while until he has had an opportunity to acquire more experience. This is the logical way of meeting failure.

[10] See the outline on page 28, which shows schematically the interrelation of these symptoms of poor personality development.

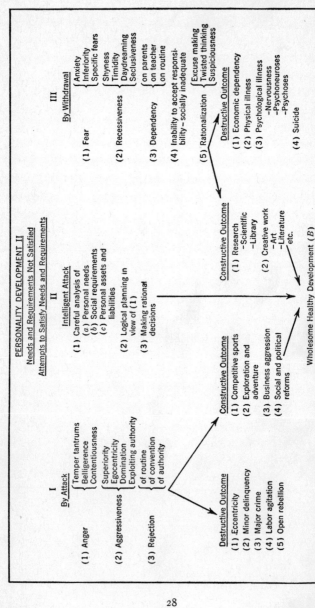

PERSONALITY DEVELOPMENT II
Needs and Requirements Not Satisfied
Attempts to Satisfy Needs and Requirements

I
By Attack

(1) Anger { Temper tantrums
             Belligerence
             Contentiousness

(2) Aggressiveness { Superiority
                     Egocentricity
                     Domination
                     Exploiting authority

(3) Rejection { of routine
                of convention
                of authority

Constructive Outcome
(1) Competitive sports
(2) Exploration and adventure
(3) Business aggression
(4) Social and political reforms

Destructive Outcome
(1) Eccentricity
(2) Minor delinquency
(3) Major crime
(4) Labor agitation
(5) Open rebellion

II
Intelligent Attack

(1) Careful analysis of
    (a) Personal needs
    (b) Social requirements
    (c) Personal assets and liabilities

(2) Logical planning in view of (1)

(3) Making rational decisions

Constructive Outcome
(1) Research
    –Scientific
    –Library
(2) Creative work
    –Art
    –Literature
    etc.

III
By Withdrawal

(1) Fear { Anxiety
           Inferiority
           Specific fears

(2) Recessiveness { Shyness
                    Timidity
                    Daydreaming
                    Seclusiveness

(3) Dependency { on parents
                 on teacher
                 on routine

(4) Inability to accept responsibility—socially inadequate

(5) Rationalization { Excuse making
                      Twisted thinking
                      Suspiciousness

Destructive Outcome
(1) Economic dependency
(2) Physical illness
(3) Psychological illness
    –Nervousness
    –Psychoneuroses
    –Psychoses
(4) Suicide

Wholesome Healthy Development (*B*)

Adapted from E. K. Wickman's *Children's Behavior and Teachers' Attitudes*, The Commonwealth Fund, New York.

28

CHAPTER III

SYMPTOMS OF POOR PERSONALITY DEVELOPMENT

I. EMOTIONAL BEHAVIOR

The Nature of Emotions. In the day-by-day behavior of the infant or the very young child we see the developing personality at a relatively simple stage; we can watch the child's behavior in relation to his attempts to satisfy his needs and meet the requirements of his environment. A one-year-old, for instance, is struggling to push open the swinging door into the kitchen. Perhaps his efforts are stimulated by his need for a fascinating new experience—the glittering array of pots and pans, the cupboards and gadgets in which the kitchen abounds. At the moment, he is completely blocked by the swinging door. He pushes it a little. It gives, but swings back on him at once. He tries cautiously once more, manages a peek into the bright kitchen before the door swings shut again. What does the child do? Usually he starts to cry. We say he is emotionally upset. It is difficult to decide what kind of emotional feeling a child of one year is experiencing. Most commonly it seems to be "just tears." We say his pride has been hurt; he has been thwarted; his self-respect has been wounded. Perhaps the child becomes very angry; then we say he has a temper tantrum. Or perhaps, if the door has swung closed a little too quickly for him, he is actually frightened. In any event, the result is usually much the same. Unless adults interfere, the child directs his interest elsewhere and turns his back on the scene of his defeat.

The nature of emotional experience and behavior is interesting because, on the surface, it appears to be inefficient. Of all the behavior possible in a given situation, a frank emotional outburst is probably the least adequate. During intense emotion, whether anger, fear, or general excitement, there is a "stirred-up" condition of the whole body. All the physiological functions are affected. The heart rate speeds up, the blood pressure rises, the secretion of the digestive juices slows down or may even stop, and many other changes occur. Scientists have suggested that these changes are adaptive in character, preparing the organism for fight or flight. In our present civilization, however, they have little value. Even in the boxing ring, intense anger is a disadvantage. Emotion inhibits the finer processes of intellect and judgment. We recognize this fact when we advise teachers to refrain, when they are angry, from punishing children.

In the infant and young child, emotional behavior may occur frequently, and in that sense is "normal"; but if it persists into later childhood or adult life, it must be considered a sign of unhealthy personality development. Actually, strong emotion is so ineffective that the "normal" child soon drops it as a method of attack on his problems.

Continued appearance of emotion in later life may be due to a number of factors. Through the intervention of parents or others, the child may discover that emotional behavior is successful in getting him what he wants. Whining, bad temper, or tears thus may be the direct result of faulty home training. Since emotion is related to physiological changes throughout the whole body, we can understand, also, how fatigue, overstimulation, or poor physical health may be major contributing factors. Sometimes emotional behavior becomes so characteristic of a child that we are tempted to assume that he was "born that way." Emotional stability is dependent on the healthy integration of the nervous system (or more strictly of that part of this system which has been called the *autonomic* or *sympathetic* nervous system), and it is possible that certain children are born with a more sensitive and more excitable nervous system than others. They will have more difficulty controlling their emotions. Emotional stability and control, however, can be achieved. They can be learned without compromising in any way the healthy development of other aspects of the whole personality.

Most of us have been in situations in which emotional behavior seemed to be inevitable. An automobile accident may arouse intense fear. An insult, suddenly and grossly thrown, will no doubt arouse anger. In such instances, emotion may not be a sign of faulty personality development. Life without emotional experiences of these kinds would be difficult, if not impossible, to achieve.

As a matter of fact, emotional experiences, in a manner and to a degree that we cannot discuss at this point, are responsible for much that is beautiful in the world. Especially is this true in the field of creative arts, where the constructive use of emotional experience is sometimes called "inspiration."

Emotional Behavior of School Children. Emotional displays in school children may be grouped roughly into three main classes. First there is *generalized excitement*. This type of emotion appears in most children if something unusual happens in the class: an important visitor, an unexpected holiday, or even an unlooked-for examination. Suppressed giggles, restless shuffling, twisting about, exclamations, and conversation are the common symptoms. Children of the sensitive, excitable type are more affected than others. Ordinarily, this type of emotional response is not undesirable. After all, life is often thrilling and exciting. In children with poor emotional control, however, these common everyday emotional incidents become exaggerated, and hysterical excitement is the result.

The other two forms of emotional behavior are of such importance that we shall discuss them at some length. They are *fear* and *anger*. Fear and anger are primitive and relatively pure emotional states. They are common and perfectly normal in infants and very young children. When they occur persistently in school-age children, they must be looked upon as being abnormal. As characteristic personality traits, they represent a sort of regression or "throwback" to infantile or immature levels of development.

Fear. The child who is continually frightened and apprehensive is easily picked out. His emotional state is betrayed by the ease with which his skin blanches, by the anxious expression on his face, and by the tendency for his hands to tremble. Such children are chronically anxious and timid, and, in addition, frequently have a large assortment of specific fears. An alarm given for fire drill terrifies them; a thunderstorm completely upsets them for the rest of the afternoon; a cross word sends them into tears. Investigation of their behavior at home will frequently reveal, among other details, that they are frightened of the dark and that they frequently have terrifying dreams at night.

A boy of nine in Grade Four was referred to the psychiatrist because of lack of progress in school, his extreme timidity, and his fearful attitude. He was a small, undernourished boy who seemed to be terrified of anything new. It was difficult to get him to talk; and when his school was mentioned, he began to cry. It was not deemed advisable to subject him to formal tests of intelligence at the time of his first interview, but his ability was estimated as low average. His teacher reported that, while he could do the work perfectly well, he did not seem able to begin and was very slow in completing his assignments. He would frequently erase, cross out, or destroy his work, rather than submit it for approval or take it home. His mother was a very large aggressive woman, who, impatient with the boy and the physician, explained the whole difficulty to her own satisfaction by the remark, "He's just lazy." In the end it was revealed that both parents were extremely ambitious and aggressive. Disappointed in their only son's rather unattractive appearance, they had exerted undue pressure and criticism at home. The boy was, by constitution, both emotionally and intellectually incapable of meeting the situation successfully.

Seldom are fear and timidity the only symptoms. More often there are many symptoms which may include such habits as stuttering, enuresis, and many of the traits to be discussed in the pages of this chapter.

While the prevention of such fears and fear-conditioned attitudes is the best remedy, once they have become established the teacher can help the child overcome them by helping him to understand them. If a child is frightened of thunderstorms, for example, the teacher can talk to him quietly and confidently about storms. On the next occasion when there is a thunderstorm he can be taken to a window where, unobserved by other children, he can watch the whole process and discuss it with his teacher objectively. The same procedure should be used in dealing with any other specific fears. Talking about frightening incidents in a way that helps the child to understand their harmlessness reduces the emotional potential.

Unfortunately, there are still teachers who are sure that a good shake and a sound scolding are the most efficient ways to deal with the frightened, timid child. Other teachers feel that their classes would be considerably better off with a few more children who had the "fear of the Lord pounded into them." A more constructive attitude would be to help such children to overcome their emotional habits. An abrupt and startling manner will certainly increase the timidity. On the other hand a too sympathetic, solicitous, and protective manner will often send these unstable children into tears again. A quiet, casual manner is best. The children should be helped individually and privately and never treated differently from the others while in the classroom.

Attitudes Related to Fear. There is a close relationship between the child who is frightened or terrified and the child who is shy, timid, and self-conscious. The former is exhibiting the primitive, more-or-less crude, emotional reaction, while the latter is showing behavior and attitudes which, while milder than primitive fear, are similar in quality. Both represent "running-away" attitudes and the desire to escape. When confronted with a difficulty which cannot readily be overcome, such children respond by withdrawing from the difficulty altogether. Rather than face up to it, they retreat into a world of their own imagination, develop feelings of inferiority, and become seclusive, sensitive, and shy. Children with these attitudes are more numerous than might be expected. A recent survey of three elementary schools showed that such children comprised about 6% of the school population.[1]

[1] A study (shortly to be published) conducted by the National Committee for Mental Hygiene (Canada), sponsored and supported by the Supreme Council 33° A∴ A∴—Scottish Rite, Northern Masonic Jurisdiction, U.S.A.

The significance of such personality characteristics as a criterion of future mental ill-health can only be surmised. It has recently been discovered that the majority of patients suffering from dementia praecox, a particularly malignant form of insanity, had this type of personality during their childhood and adolescence. This fact does not mean that all (or even the majority) of children who manifest fear-conditioned attitudes in marked form are destined to become seriously mentally ill. But there undoubtedly is some danger in the persistence and growth of such attitudes and their continuation into adulthood. The shy and timid child is seldom found among the "bad" pupils, who cause so much trouble with their noisy, aggressive misbehavior. On the contrary, they are commonly found among the "best" pupils—children whose conduct and application are excellent, and who rank high in their schoolwork. It is precisely for this reason that their emotional immaturity is so often overlooked. In talking of such a child, a teacher recently said, "Why, Jean is such a nice quiet little thing, you would never know she was in the class. She is really a model child—and *so* sensitive." While these children may not be "problems" to the teacher, they are frequently problems to themselves; and they require a good deal of understanding and thoughtful concern. It will be useful to describe more fully their most characteristic symptoms.

(*a*) *Shyness and seclusiveness.* The most frequent characteristic of the "withdrawing" child is shyness. Shyness is not often regarded by teachers with much concern. It interferes with class routine only when the pupil is required to answer questions or take part in class activities. Some teachers actually encourage shyness as a sign of desirable modesty, although sometimes it seems to be not so much modesty as conceit. Shyness and self-consciousness usually indicate that the child (or adult) is so preoccupied with himself that he believes everyone is paying attention to him.

The shy child is frequently a lonely child. He seems unable to mix with other children so as to enjoy himself in their company, but hangs back on the fringe of activities. At recess he attempts to remain inside or else stands around by himself watching the others play. Away from school he may show the same characteristics. Instead of playing with other children, he goes to his own home and plays by himself. He is reluctant to participate in sports or games. In fact there do not seem to be many things that he likes to do. He is quiet, solitary, and usually friendless. In addition, he is often very sensitive.

Shyness and seclusiveness must be regarded as symptoms of maladjustment—of the child's retreat from a tiresome or even intolerable situation. The teacher and the school can do a great deal to help such a child, when the underlying cause of the trouble is discovered. Usually the fundamental difficulty lies in complete lack of self-confidence and a deep feeling of inferiority with respect to some real or imagined personal inadequacy. With boys, lack of physical strength, smallness of stature, clumsiness, and lack of skill in games are likely to give rise to these feelings. A child who is awkward at sports, for example, is the object of teasing and ridicule. He comes to look upon himself as weak, peculiar, and different. Such experiences are unpleasant, and so, by withdrawal, he avoids their recurrence. With girls, the difficulty is commonly a matter of unattractive features. Physical disabilities, such as deformities, birthmarks, protruding teeth, or poorly balanced eye muscles, and special disabilities, such as a defect in speech or a reading difficulty, may be contributory factors.

Sometimes a child's feelings of inferiority are associated with a conviction of his own dullness and stupidity. This may have reference to his schoolwork as a whole or to some particular subject only. Constant competition with brighter children and the resulting inevitable and continuous failure help to foster this conviction. Speed tests are particularly vicious in this respect.

A child may be unduly sensitive about his economic background and social talents. Feelings of inferiority may thus arise because of a poor home, inability to make friends, to dance well, or to feel at ease in a social gathering. A conflict of social customs and culture frequently occurs in the children of "foreign" parents. All these factors are dealt with more specifically in later sections.

As effective as these factors are in the development of a child's timidity, they become seriously aggravated if, in addition, the child is exposed to scorn, ridicule, harsh criticism, and punishment.

The teacher's treatment of these shy, seclusive children should be directed towards correcting the cause of the difficulty.[2]

An eleven-year-old girl was doing fair work in Grade Six and was regarded by the teacher as being one of the "very nicest" girls in the class. She would never have been singled out for examination had not the psychologist discussed, by chance, the shy, seclusive type of child with the teacher. She immediately mentioned this child as possibly being one of this type, and agreed to observe her closely for a week. She was amazed at what she discovered. When she was asking questions

[2] The method of determining the cause of the difficulty will be discussed in detail in the next chapter.

MH-4

of the class, she observed that the girl hid her head behind the pupil in front, so as to escape being called upon to answer. If she had to answer a question, she blushed and spoke in a very hushed voice. The slightest criticism from the teacher usually sent her to the verge of tears. She did not have any friends, and yet, in talking to the other children, the teacher was unable to discover any real reason why they avoided her. During recess and after school, she never played or talked with other children. She would come early to school and stay late.

After making friends with the child, the teacher found that the child constantly tried to be near her. The girl would always wait to walk home with her. The only activity which she seemed to enjoy was to play by herself with her dolls in a corner of her own attic. An investigation of her background at home showed that her father was a successful professional man, with a keen and critical mind. He was never enthusiastic about anything the girl did, and left her upbringing to an intelligent but rather unsympathetic stepmother. It was evident that the girl was retreating from both the home and school situations and was finding it increasingly difficult to play with anyone. Naturally an affectionate child, she had not adequate emotional outlet; and when the teacher became interested in her, she at once adopted her as a sort of "mother-person." The psychologist's examination revealed that she had rather exceptional ability. Her I.Q. was 134. Her achievement in school, although good, was by no means up to what the girl was able to do. With the aid of the excellent relationship existing between the teacher and the pupil, the child was helped to enjoy play and social situations. The teacher appealed directly to a group of intelligent girls in the class; and they took it upon themselves to help the child and to make her one of their friends. Fortunately, she responded well, and finally joined a girls' club at her church. This helped to re-establish her social interests. In classwork the teacher discovered a latent ability in music, and through this was able to give her special satisfactions in allowing her to organize a music club. With her social improvement, her interest and success in classwork has increased steadily.

Probably the most important single thing for the teacher to do is to make sure that the child achieves success in a fair proportion of his tasks. It is impossible to expect healthy, wholesome personalities in children who invariably come last in everything they attempt. The child who is seclusive must be helped to enjoy social contacts. As a rule he literally has to be *taught* to play. It is useless to force the child into social situations, for this makes participation a disagreeable duty, imposed by an outside authority. The teacher can, however, show the child how to enjoy his first real social experience. The event may have to be fairly insignificant at first in order to ensure participation by the child. Once the child begins to take an interest, the battle is nearly won; for nothing succeeds like success, and nothing is so convincing to the child as an actual demonstration of his ability to enjoy himself with others.

Finally, in working with shy and recessive children, it should be remembered that our goal is not necessarily to develop overconfidence and aggressiveness. There is a place in the world for shy people. We count the end result excellent, therefore, if we are able to engender in these children a feeling of poise and equanimity.

(*b*) *Daydreaming.* All children daydream. The teacher recognizes such behavior as "woolgathering" or "inattention." In some children it is a transient occurrence, indicative only of the lack of anything more interesting to do. In others, however, it represents a means of escaping an unpleasant or intolerable situation. When children withdraw from such situations, and take refuge in their own fantasies and "castles-in-Spain," they are probably attempting to satisfy some basic but neglected need. The fantasies become more absorbing, enjoyable, and satisfying than reality with its never-ending problems. When daydreaming becomes a substitute for normal effort, it is then a symptom of maladjustment.

However, not all children who are inattentive or who have vacant expressions are daydreaming. A child may be "miles away" and yet be working on the solution of some complex problem that is immediately pertinent to his school adjustment. On the other hand, it is not always correct to assume that a child is not daydreaming just because he seems to be busy at his desk. Children generally learn that at least a semblance of activity is required, and as long as they go through the motions, they know they have little chance of being disturbed in their fantasies.

The constructive and positive approach of the teacher to such problems is, first of all, to discover the cause. There must be a reason for excessive daydreaming. The root of the trouble may be in the school situation, or it may go back to the home. Harsh, threatening, unsympathetic parents frequently bring up sensitive children who adopt this type of behavior. Sometimes difficulties and failures at school lead such a child to seek satisfaction and security in a retreat to daydreaming. Sometimes the mechanism is just the reverse—the school situation is too easy for the child and presents no real challenge to his interest and effort. Frequently much can be learned by encouraging the child to talk about his daydreams. They are usually a type of wishful thinking, and the content of the fantasies may provide a clue to the cause of the trouble. Children who have not been ridiculed or scolded about their daydreams will not be reluctant to discuss them with a sympathetic friend.

Once the child's confidence has been obtained, and the nature of the fantasies has been established, it is fairly easy to be constructive. The general aim should be to help the child to carry his daydreams over into action. This can be done by allowing him to experience the thrill of real success and achievement. Compared with this, the imaginary successes are colorless and unimportant. Environmental interests, such as games and recreational pursuits, can be added gradually to the child's activities. The teacher should make sure that the child deals with each activity in at least a partially successful and satisfying way.

There are a few things to avoid in dealing with the daydreaming child. Criticism, ridicule, or punishment should never be used. The child is already dissatisfied with his real world and is retreating from its unpleasantness. Physical or mental pain inflicted by the annoyed teacher will only increase that unpleasantness. Too much insistence on silence in the classroom and a too-frequent use of isolation as a means of punishment are practices which actually encourage the tendency.

An attractive-looking boy of nine in Grade Three was brought to the attention of the school psychologist because he was constantly in a "daze." Investigation showed that the teacher was having difficulty in gaining and holding his attention. It was not a question of his doing other things when he was supposed to be listening to her, so much as the fact that he seemed to be daydreaming and brooding. The only way the teacher was able to obtain and hold his attention was to speak sharply to him. On these occasions he would "come to" with a start, and seem vaguely annoyed and just a bit sullen.

Further inquiry showed that, in addition to his daydreaming, this lad was a shy child who lacked confidence in himself. He was a slow learner, his I.Q. being 92. His academic achievements were consistently poor. His worst subjects were reading and arithmetic. Out of school hours he played nicely with his younger sister and two or three small children in his neighborhood. He never played with the boys of his own age, chiefly because they called him "sissy" and teased him about the fact that he had no father. The home situation was interesting. The father had deserted the family when the boy was six. The mother had directed all her love and attention to her two small children, and as a consequence they were suffering from a considerable amount of overprotection. In addition to this, the mother was very ambitious for the boy and was critical of his bad reports. She constantly urged him to "try to do better for Mother's sake." Unhappy in his social relationships with other children, and frustrated by his inability to succeed at school, the lad was taking refuge in his daydreams.

Having obtained the child's confidence, the psychologist was able to get him to tell about his fantasies. He liked to think of himself as being a bold and successful hero, who, after making his fortune, returned to his mother and established her as a sort of queen, where all the people of his acquaintanceship, including his teacher and the boys who had teased him, came to pay homage. The psychologist and the teacher worked out methods of helping him to experience real situations, rather than imaginary ones. The work in arithmetic and reading was adjusted to his ability, so that for several weeks in a row he obtained perfect marks. Having re-established his self-confidence, the boy became more sociable and more interested in his work and play, both in the classroom and outside. A summer camp continued the treatment, and he is now on his way to an excellent adjustment.

Anger. Primitive anger behavior as it occurs at two or three years of age is occasionally seen in older children.

The immediate cause of such a display is usually frustration. The child is prevented from doing something he wants to do, or is made to do something he does not want to do. The school-age child who reacts to such situations with a show of temper is evading the real issue by reverting to a type of behavior which was sometimes successful in similar situations when he was younger.

The angry child may attack an obstacle other than the one which is really causing the difficulty. A boy during an art class, for example, wanted to decorate his painting with some gold paint which he had stored in his desk. The teacher, her good taste outraged, refused permission; whereupon the boy, in a temper, tore up his "creation" into a hundred pieces. This behavior was indeed in the nature of an attack; but it was not directed to his real problem, the thwarting of his own wishes by the ruling of the teacher. Whether the teacher was wise in her ruling is another matter.

The manifestations of temper or anger are varied. They may include all kinds of spectacular acts such as breath-holding, kicking, and screaming, abusive language, and even physical attacks on the teacher. These bad-tempered children can be dealt with only by firmness. Since the habit becomes more difficult with each recurrence, it is important to try to settle the trouble once and for all the first time it comes up. If the child is sullen or gives a display of temper, he should be helped to return to normal behavior quietly and by himself. It is a favor to the child to isolate him for a time. Isolation does not save the child's face, but it does give him a chance to "cool off." If the opportunity to cool off is not provided, the tantrum may be followed by argument, sullenness, obstinacy, or other variations of the pure anger reaction. For his own sake, as well as for the sake of the class whose peace he is disturbing, the angry child should be promptly banished.

Banishment without provision for a definite room for exile is not isolation. The hall outside the classroom door does not offer isolation. Every school should have a counsel room where child and teacher may talk privately. At the end of the lesson, the teacher should go to the child and in a quiet but firm manner should indicate that no behavior of this type will be tolerated in the class. Then the teacher should forget the incident, let the child come back, and for the next two days be as helpful and kind as possible. A public apology before the class is absolutely unnecessary and unwarranted. If the teacher's prestige is so shaky, and his pride so sensitive that an apology is demanded, then he is more at fault than the child. If he secures the co-operation of the child, however, by giving him opportunity for successful achievement, the teacher will probably have no further problem with that child. It goes without saying that in all such situations the teacher must keep his own temper. There may be some justification for the teacher's occasionally *pretending* to be angry, but there is certainly none for *actually* becoming so.

Attitudes Related to Anger. Just as shyness, timidity, daydreaming, and seclusiveness are related to fear and the attempt to escape or retreat from the fear-provoking situation, so, in children, there are certain traits and attitudes related to anger. Children characterized by the various types of the anger-attitude are far less likely to be overlooked by the teacher than are those with more retiring dispositions. The former are the "problem" children of the class, the "bad boys" and the bullies. They are the boastful show-offs who are continually striving for attention. Analyzing such behavior a little more carefully, we usually find, paradoxically, that these children are reacting to frustration which threatens their self-esteem and security. They seem to be reacting to their feelings of inferiority in a manner just the opposite of that used by children who withdraw and retreat from difficulties. For example, a situation brings about feelings of personal inadequacy. To admit these inadequacies would be to admit defeat and failure, which would be even more intolerable. Rather than retreat, the child makes a vigorous defense by attack. But instead of making a direct attack on the threatening difficulty, he evades it by adopting an aggressive, boastful pose. Thus feelings of superiority that we see in children are frequently generated by a more basic feeling of inferiority. The child is said to be compensating for his real or imaginary inadequacy. Frequently he goes the whole way, does not compensate just a little for his failure or frustration, but extravagantly *overcompensates* so that, in the class at any rate, he is indeed a problem.

(*a*) *Bullying and teasing*. This type of behavior is observed most frequently in boys. Those who are older and larger than their group select smaller, younger children as objects of aggression. Sometimes the bullying takes on an aspect of physical cruelty. The smaller boys are buffeted and pinched, have their fingers bent back and their ears pulled.

Since this type of aggressive behavior is an *overcompensation* for failure or threatened failure, the various special disabilities listed in the section on "Shyness and seclusiveness" (page 35) are again the chief causative factors. Occasionally children who bully are imitating their own parents. Thus a child may have been the victim of unjustifiable aggression on the part of the father. Unable to attack his father, he "takes it out" on smaller children. He may even secretly admire his father for his domineering attitudes, and attempt to demonstrate his own superiority in the same way.

(b) *Playing for attention.* One of the commonest ways in which a child overcompensates is by making a play for the spotlight of attention. He is not only aggressive in his attitude towards others, but also boasts, "shows off," and in other ways tries to make himself conspicuous. Occasionally he tries to demonstrate his superiority by making the other children laugh. If the child cannot gain the spotlight by his success in schoolwork, sports, or social events, he may try other, less desirable, methods. Frequently the fuss which his misbehavior causes is exactly the result he desires to bring about. And if he is finally given corporal punishment, he may actually enjoy the ceremony that gives him, for a few minutes at least, the very center of the stage. Punitive discipline frequently caters to this tendency.

(c) *Negativism.* One of the most troublesome problems in the classroom is disobedience, or refusal to conform or comply with authoritative requests. This type of behavior is sometimes called *negativism,* and may be manifested in sullen stubbornness, contrariness, contradictory attitudes, and even outright rebellion against authority. For example, a five-year-old girl in the kindergarten was flagrantly disobedient and obstinate. She quarreled with the other children and was vicious in her methods of attack. She threw a small chair at the teacher, and tried to poke another child with a pair of scissors. For three days she resolutely refused to do anything in class except sit;

she did not speak to either the teacher or the children. Her behavior was that of "defense by attack," the schoolroom analogy to a sit-down strike. It was a demonstration of aggressive behavior used as a compensation for insecurity.

It should be made perfectly clear that a child does not deliberately plan his bad behavior to compensate for inadequacy or to gain attention. Compensation may be the fundamental process at work and should be considered by the teacher in any attempt to understand the logic of the child's behavior; but, to the child, his own bad behavior is quite inexplicable. He is responding to an unconscious urge that has either an immediate or a remote history of inadequacy.

The constructive handling of such problems depends on the teacher's insight into the causes. Whenever possible, the cause should be discovered and removed. Bullying and excessive teasing, for example, represent not so much a case for the strap as a case for investigation. Of course, while investigation proceeds, the freedom and rights of the other children in the class have to be protected. To this end, it may be necessary to isolate the aggressive child during play periods until the cause has been determined and constructive measures have had time to take effect. Some of these measures will be discussed at length below. Their purpose is the provision of adequate opportunities for legitimate successful development. Many, perhaps most, of these opportunities can be obtained within the school and classroom. Where opportunity lends itself, the teacher can help the child to develop outside interests and recreational outlets, which will help him to control and direct positively some of his aggressive tendencies. Such group activities as the

Y.M.C.A., the Scouts, and church clubs of various sorts are valuable for boys of this type.[3]

An illustrative instance may show the value of investigation and demonstrate the relation of cause to remedial measures.

A good-looking boy, seven years old, in Grade Two, was reported by the school as being a nuisance because of his swaggering boastful attitude and his "nosy" interference with other children. He always wanted to play with bigger boys and butt into their affairs, so that they treated him roughly and rolled him in the snow. His intelligence was of a good average quality, his schoolwork fairly satisfactory; but his teacher found him difficult because of his continued efforts to show off.

Investigation revealed some interesting facts concerning his background. His father had deserted the family soon after the boy was born. His mother had found it difficult to accept the child because it meant a restriction of her own social life. The physical environment was inadequate, and when the boy developed rickets his mother gladly turned him over to the Children's Aid Society and showed no further interest in him. After six months in the Children's Shelter, he was placed, at the age of two, with a foster mother who really wanted him as a playmate and toy for her own four-year-old son. She soon tired of him and returned him to the home; later she took him back again, only to return him once more. By this time he was four years old. The Society then placed him with a man and wife who were anxious to adopt him. Two years later they had not completed adoption papers; and when he exhibited his aggressive traits, they threatened to send him back to "The Home." His behavior seemed to be an attempt at compensating for his feelings of inadequacy and lack of emotional security. He wanted very much to love someone as his mother and to have a home to which he belonged. This was demonstrated

[3] For a fuller discussion of the use of these facilities, see Chapter VIII.

when he kept asking the social worker for reassurance: "This is my home, isn't it?" "I don't have to go to another home, do I?"

An effort was made to explain the situation to the foster parents and to the teacher. All agreed to help to supply some of the security that was so obviously lacking. Adoption papers were completed, a membership in the Y.M.C.A. was arranged, and an opportunity provided in the classroom dramatics for him to achieve distinction legitimately. He is still under supervision.

II. EXCUSE MAKING OR RATIONALIZING

In addition to emotional displays and attitudes, faulty personality development is revealed by excessive rationalization or excuse making. Rationalization is the child's habit of finding logical reasons to justify himself in doing something that is not in accord with the standards of action he usually accepts. Or conversely, it is the finding of logical reasons for not doing something which under ordinary circumstances the child would have considered the necessary and right thing to do. It is, therefore, the attempt, too often successful, to silence or pervert the promptings of what is often called a "conscience" (or more specifically, a "sense of values"). A child resorts to the procedure usually to escape blame for misconduct. Very often the rationalization is subsequent to an emotional reaction or attitude of a type considered in the previous paragraphs. In this case it represents an attempt to explain, in a logical and reasonable way, the behavior or the fundamental failure that so often underlies the emotional reaction.

Parents and teachers may encourage children to develop the habit by emphasis on the importance of having a good reason for everything the children do. Thus children early form the habit of making excuses for their shortcomings, either to satisfy themselves, or, it may be, to escape the consequences.

A "sour-grapes" attitude is a form of rationalization generally learned as a method of self-justification and fact-dodging without actual lying. Another kind of rationalizing, less frequently discussed, is the "sweet-lemon" attitude. Here a child suffering from some disadvantage frankly enjoys it, and states he would not have it otherwise. This is a bad habit to encourage. If a child is lame, he should not be told that his disability is really an advantage. It is healthier to teach him to face his problem frankly and to seek acceptable channels of activity.

Blaming Other People. One of the most unhealthy types of rationalization is the tendency to justify oneself and one's conduct by blaming other people. Psychologists call this "projection." It means simply that a person, consciously or unconsciously, projects the cause of his inadequate performance (or sometimes the inadequate performance itself) onto some other person. This method of evasion is common in adults as well as in children. Child and adult, Adam-like, are too frequently content to direct the burden of blame to the shoulders of someone else. Happy the teacher who has not been blamed, quite unfairly, by child or parent for a pupil's failure or misconduct.

In the day-to-day misconduct of pupils, the teacher's attitude toward blame is basically responsible for many instances of projection. Too strong an emphasis on determining the actual responsibility for this misdemeanor or that will almost inevitably encourage the children to put the blame on someone else. If the emotional situation is tense enough, and the children in the class sufficiently aroused, such projection is more than half believed by the child himself. This tendency actually to believe the rationalization takes the projection out of the realm of frank lying to escape consequences, which, of course, it most closely resembles.

Exceptional Virtue. Another interesting type of behavior commonly seen in children is an extraordinary zeal to be virtuous. The child, as it were, agrees to do all the things that good children should do, and to do them with meticulous care, if the teacher, in turn, will overlook some of his shortcomings in the actual work of the classroom. Such traits as excessive neatness, courtesy, and honesty, for example, represent such an attitude.

A boy returned a lost article that he had found. While he was returning the article he made many protestations of the virtue of being honest, and how, if he had been dishonest, he might have kept it, and so forth. Another child was excessively and painfully neat in all her written work. She spent literally hours erasing slight mistakes and making sure that the ruled lines were just right. These children would seem to be compensating for a feeling of failure in some other field.

Some teachers tend to emphasize certain traits unduly, and thus encourage this sort of evasion. Neatness, after all, is not so important in itself. Like honesty and courtesy, it should be accepted as the normal, expected thing. Some children show excessive anxiety over ordinary mistakes, and an extreme concern over criticism and failure. Such overconscientiousness is not a healthy attitude. Failure is inevitable, and everyone should experience it and profit by it. If individuals can regard it objectively, and without emotion, and if they can benefit from it so as to avoid similar failures in the future, then failure will have a true mental-hygiene value.

III. NERVOUSNESS

There is a type of poor personality development which is so extensive and which includes so many and varying "symptoms" that it must be described separately. In adults these symptoms may be so troublesome to the patient and so obvious to others that the psychiatrist looks upon the condition as a sort of illness. He calls it a *psychoneurosis*. Psychoneurotic behavior of adults may include a variety of nervous mannerisms, tics, indecisions, worries, obsessions, and even invalidism, as well as habits such as enuresis and stuttering. The only reason for placing these types of behavior in a group apart from those formerly described is that they tend on the whole to be less obvious in their origin and frequently more spectacular in their manifestations. Fundamentally they are the same. They are evidences of emotional and social maldevelopment. Many psychiatrists would classify all the symptoms described in this chapter as psychoneurotic in form; and some would limit this term to a few well-defined forms seen more frequently among adults, and conditioned by a complex of circumstances. But the name, after all, is not important.

In children, psychoneurotic symptoms appear as "nervousness." Just as the psychiatrist includes under *psychoneurosis* a large number of varying symptoms, so the teacher is likely to use "nervousness" as a descriptive term for a number of different conditions. The teacher may mean that the child is immature and infantile, or that he is irritable, tense, and overactive, or that he is timid, fearful, and overanxious. The danger in the use of the term is that once the tag of "nervousness" is attached to a child, the teacher is likely to think he has diagnosed the condition and fully explained it. Actually, to label a child "nervous," and leave it at that, is little better than to diagnose "stomach-ache" without seeking to trace the abdominal pain to its specific (and possibly very serious) cause. The teacher is making the same sort of error as the general practitioner who comes to the conclusion that his worried and vaguely ill patient is "just a neurotic." The diagnostic and remedial procedures begin, rather than end, at this point. Why is the child nervous? Why is he showing psychoneurotic symptoms? What can be done about them?

It is true that a few children seem to be "born nervous." They are suffering from no disease of the nerves; they are constitutionally tense, restless, and hyperactive. Actually these cases are rare; and most children who are supposedly "born nervous" have really developed this trait through outside influences. The power of suggestion is particularly important. Often the parents start the trouble by speaking of the child as being "high-strung" or "shy." If they continue to describe him in these terms, the child himself finally comes to believe in them, and does his best to live up to his reputation. It is, therefore, a good general rule in dealing with the "nervous" child to treat him as if he were normal, and thus help him to dispel the notion that he is different. This does not mean that no positive measures should be taken. Much can be done by so building up the general situation that the child's behavior ceases to cause difficulty. The following brief discussion of the common manifestations of nervousness, with suggestions concerning helpful attitudes and constructive procedures on the part of the

teacher, will indicate how the treatment of the cases may
be facilitated.

Some Signs of Nervousness. The commonest sign of
nervousness seen in childhood is a generalized over-
activity and restlessness. The child seemingly is unable
to sit still or to pay attention to one thing for very long
at a time. He fidgets and bounces around in his seat; and
he can become a very disturbing influence in the classroom. Sometimes he is boisterous and noisy, and often he
is extremely mischievous. Along with these nervous manifestations, signs of emotional instability are frequently
seen. Thus the child, in addition to being restless, may be
irritable and cranky or easily moved to tears.

The nervous child is frequently the worried child.
Sometimes he seems to be carrying the world's troubles
on his back. He worries about his parents, his little
brother, the family's financial condition, and many other
things, which, to adults, seem trivial and absurd. He does
not seem able to do anything to solve his problems or
meet his difficulties; nor does he try to evade them by
some subterfuge such as a compensating aggressiveness.
He is so worried and anxious that he cannot make up his
mind about anything. This constant emotional activity
results in a persistent state of tension, so that the child
may react excessively even to the smallest stimuli (such
as a faint sound or his name quietly spoken by the
teacher).

Nervous mannerisms are frequently seen in such children. These mannerisms vary from quick involuntary
muscular movements, such as grimacing or blinking the
eyelids, to movements of a voluntary sort, more widespread in action, such as rubbing the nose or scratching
the head. Careful observation has shown that one or other

of these little habits is present in almost all school children. They become a problem, however, when they are so obvious that they are a distraction to the other pupils or a handicap to the child himself. The most common types of mannerisms are those having to do with the mouth, such as nail biting or thumb sucking. Twitching and blinking of the eyelids are also quite frequently encountered.

The cause of these nervous habits is not always known. Some of them may begin as quite useful and purposeful movements, the kind that are directed toward a local irritation, for instance. After many repetitions they become habits. The children themselves are frequently unaware of their occurrence. Some of the very quick automatic movements or tics may have their origin in an overexcitable nervous system. It is often difficult to distinguish clearly between nervous tics of this kind and the restless jerking movements of chorea (St. Vitus's dance), which is really a disease of the nervous system. The responsibility for the differentiation should be left to the physician. Underlying many of these signs of nervousness is the fact that the child is suffering from too much emotional tension. We have seen that innate nervous instability may be a factor here. Nevertheless, it is true that environmental situations, such as a broken home, too many restrictions, and too much stress on academic progress and success, may create such emotional tension. Modern apartments where the "no-noise" rule is rigidly enforced contribute to the nervousness of children. If, added to this, the school follows a formalized teaching procedure, or fails even to allow free expression of animal spirits, such children are likely to be thwarted all the time.

Teaching Nervous Children. Almost any sort of interesting constructive activity will help to reduce nervous tension. Changes in the programs of study which have recently been made in many parts of the United States and Canada widen the scope of activities available to the children. It is true that when such a nervous child becomes intently interested in work or play, his worry and most of his "nervousness" seem to disappear. Sometimes the teacher must help the child to find some constructive activity which interests him. In this connection the teacher might benefit from the experience of psychiatric clinics for children. Such creative materials as clay, plasticine, paints, crayons, and drawing paper are particularly valuable. Through these mediums the nervous child expresses himself in a way that reduces his emotional tension.

One high-strung child was recently enrolled in a children's class at the Art Gallery. An interested teacher took him under her wing and encouraged him to express some of his thoughts and feelings in color and line. The rather spectacular result was a series of creations with such titles as "Music and Rhythm," "The Wind on a Cloudy Day," "Voices Talking Too Loudly," and others. The interpretations were excellently done, and the result was really artistic. The most interesting result, however, was the poise, confidence, and stability developed by the child. It was as if he had been able to express through the medium of his art, his pent-up emotional energy, thus bringing relief of tension.

Some of these children are more quickly attracted to the task of "making things"; and here the teacher can borrow ideas from the occupational therapist. The older, more conventional forms of practical activity, such as manual training and household science, are rapidly being broadened to include a host of simple creative interests. Weaving, leatherwork, and metalwork are samples of the kind of thing that can be done in the ordinary schoolroom. If curriculums and classroom procedures permit of their use in connection with the regular work of the school, so much the better.

One word of warning. In constructive and creative activity, the child must be encouraged *really* to create. From the psychiatric point of view, and probably the educational as well, to teach an art lesson in the conventional way, or to encourage a child to copy a drawing or a model, is not enough. The teacher must encourage these children to *express* their own thoughts in *their own way* and in their own mediums. The only motivation they need is the encouragement to make *something*. The only limitations are those of time, place, and social conformity.

Similar creative expression can be exercised in plays, debates, and games. It may seem odd to say that a nervous child should be encouraged to take part in such exhibitions; but the secret of success lies in allowing activity and participation to grow naturally—encouraged, but not forced. There are so many things to be done in preparation for these activities, quite apart from the actual performance, that plays and debates provide an ideal basis for the development of confidence and self-control.

In addition to this general educational approach there are several principles of treatment for nervousness to be kept in mind. The old idea that the nervous child always requires a quiet and sheltered environment is not true. There are always exceptions, of course, but in clinical experience the great majority of nervous children benefit by full programs of interesting activity that includes ample opportunity for noisy, boisterous play. It is true, however, that fatigue sometimes contributes to nervousness; hence an effort should be made to ensure adequate rest. Nervous children need more sleep than normal children, and usually they get less. The necessary amount of sleep varies according to age, but for children up to ten or eleven years of age it should not fall much below twelve hours a night. In some cases, to establish good sleeping habits, a doctor may prescribe a mild sedative in hot milk to be taken by the child before he goes to bed. But sedatives should never be used as routine measures.

As for tics and nervous mannerisms, anyone who, himself, has tried to overcome such habits will realize how very difficult it is to conquer them. Punishment and scolding only fix the habits more firmly, as a rule. Since tics and mannerisms tend to become worse when the emotional tension is increased, treatment should be directed not toward increasing the emotional strain but toward reducing and relieving it. In addition to the use of educational procedures described above, the teacher should arrange for the co-operation of the rest of the class. Teasing the child about his habit should be absolutely "taboo." The co-operation of the parents, also, in developing at home a similar attitude of sympathy and understanding, is almost essential if the habit is not to persist indefinitely.

Compulsive Behavior. Sometimes the symptoms of emotional maladjustment take the form of queer habits of thinking and acting. A child's insistence on touching every picket in a fence as he walks along, and a careful avoidance of stepping on cracks in the sidewalk lest he should "break his mother's back" are mild examples of compulsive behavior. They occur so commonly in children that they can hardly be called abnormal. They have their counterpart, also, in adult behavior. Who, among our readers, has not worried for fear the back door has been left unlocked, even when it has been examined two or three times? Who has not felt the compelling urge to return just once more to make sure that the window has been closed or that the gas has been turned off? We realize, perhaps, that our anxiety is absurd, that the door certainly is locked and everything is in order. But we feel we must return once more to go through the business of making sure. This feeling of *compulsion* to act in a certain way, when exaggerated, can become serious. When the symptom takes the form of distressing thought, which recurs despite all efforts "to put it out of mind," it is called an *obsession*.

We do not have to look far for dramatic clinical examples of this type of "nervousness." Commonly at psychiatric clinics people appear who are suffering from the feeling that their hands are contaminated and must be washed every few minutes. At the clinic a man explains that he is tortured by the fear that a terrible catastrophe will befall him if he dares to leave his home during daylight. Such severe disorders seldom occur in childhood; but the following illustration is typical of the kind of difficulty occasionally encountered:

A good-looking Polish boy of twelve was referred to the clinic because of peculiar behavior. A review of his history showed that he was an only child who had developed a strong emotional attachment to his mother. The mother suffered from tuberculosis and had been removed to a sanatorium, where she died rather suddenly. Without any preparation the lad was taken to the funeral by his grief-stricken father. It was his first experience with death. For weeks afterwards he brooded constantly about his mother, death, and the hereafter. He began to take a morbid interest in disease processes, and asked questions continually about the possibility of bringing a body back to life. Attempts by well-meaning friends to give him an understanding of the religious significance of death met with scoffing resistance. One night he went to his mother's grave with the intention of digging up her coffin and making at least one attempt to bring her back to life. He became more and more preoccupied with the problem, and more and more confused. His schoolwork was completely neglected. Everything he saw or heard seemed to have some special significance for him concerning death. He was suffering from a typical obsession.

Symptoms of this type and severity are really problems for the specialist. The teacher can do no more than try to be understanding and sympathetic. Certainly criticism, ridicule, and punishment should be avoided. A frank but confidential conversation with the child will nearly always be helpful. The conversation should be directed along the line of the child's interests and attitudes, his loves and hates, the things he likes to do and the things he finds difficult. In such an interview, the teacher should be careful to discuss seriously and carefully any questions which the child raises. Common-sense explanations are usually indicated. In any event, in a private, friendly interview the teacher can nearly always gain the child's confidence. The problems bothering the child should be discussed seriously and carefully. The technique of the personal interview is discussed fully in a later chapter.[4]

Convenient Illnesses. It is possible to evade difficulties by becoming physically ill. It is so easy and respectable to avoid an unpleasant task by pleading a bad headache. Such a complaint is much more acceptable to the person

---

[4] See page 94.

himself and to his friends than the unpleasant emotional experiences associated with an unsuccessful attack on the problem.[5] In children the retreat into illness is usually a superficial mechanism, and since it is a natural reaction, it is easily understood. Children in most homes receive attention and sympathy when they are ill. It is a delightful experience for the child to realize that his welfare causes concern and that the slightest sign of new distress or pain brings anxious faces around him. When he is really seriously ill he is usually suffering too much to enjoy such personal attention, but when he reaches convalescence he manifestly enjoys himself. The result is almost always a prolongation of the period of convalescence, and frequently a tendency to reproduce the symptoms. In some children even the slightest symptom of illness is likely to be exaggerated for the child's advantage, either to obtain a break from school or to attract sympathy and attention to himself.

In the classroom the teacher will soon recognize those children who, often unwittingly, use illness to evade their difficulties. Once the teacher suspects such a condition he is likely to think of it as deliberate malingering; and the treatment for malingering is usually punishment. In nervous children, punishment is a mistake. Far from eradicating the behavior, punishment has the reverse effect. If the child, by his punishment, becomes emotionally upset to a sufficient degree, the symptoms may begin

[5] Of course, the mechanism of the illness is not always so obvious or so simple as this. The difficulty may reside in a deep and fundamental thwarting of such a nature as to be repressed from consciousness. It may be too dreadful to think about. In such a case, the symptoms of illness are produced in the body as a result of the effort to reduce the emotional tension. The symptoms of physical illness which result are regarded by the individual as truly physical in their origin and are real in their unpleasant manifestations.

to have some basis in fact. Certainly the headache that follows prolonged worry or irritation is a common enough example of what an excited state of the emotions can do to provide real physical symptoms.

A girl of thirteen in Grade Six had normal intelligence but was not fitting into the classroom situation very well. She was described by her teacher as having a "vicious temper." One day when the teacher was reprimanding her for disturbing the class, she lost her temper and began to "talk back." The teacher asked her to come to the front of the room. She stood up by her desk and immediately fell down in what appeared to be a dead faint. The teacher, surprised and alarmed, called the school nurse and between them they carried the girl to the rest room, where, after a great deal of commotion and excitement, the girl recovered. She explained afterwards that she was in the habit of taking these "fainting spells" at home whenever she became too excited. A careful investigation revealed the fact that fainting spells did occur at home, usually when the mother was scolding her or insisting that she do something she did not want to do. A careful physical examination revealed no organic cause for the spells. When the principal gained the child's confidence and was able to interpret her behavior for her in a kindly way, the fainting spells diminished and finally disappeared. The girl herself was only dimly aware of the purposive nature of her spells.

In every case of this type, medical opinion is desirable. If the physician considers that there is no organic basis for the illness, he may leave to the teacher the task of discovering why the child is having symptoms. What purpose is being served? If the child is only anxious to gain sympathy and attract attention to himself, the teacher can deal with the situation quietly, alone with the child. If it is a question of evading disagreeable schoolwork, there are many ways of making the work more attractive. The only requirements, on the part of the teacher, are a healthy imagination and an understanding of children.

Occasionally more serious forms of illness caused by psychological factors are encountered in the classroom. Such conditions as hysterical blindness, paralysis, or even convulsions have been reported from time to time in school children. The differentiation between these types of illness and illness caused by definite physical disease is often difficult and is outside the realm of the teacher's responsibility. They are dealt with at greater length in a later chapter.[6]

IV. STUTTERING

The Nature of Stuttering. There are many kinds of speech defects. Some of them are caused by malformation of the mouth and throat, some by definite diseases of the nervous system.[7] The most common type of speech defect, however, is caused either by faulty training or by emotional difficulty and appears as stuttering or stammering. Stuttering is but another symptom of poor personality development, similar to "tics" and nervous mannerisms. Like nervous mannerisms, stuttering, once developed, may continue long after the circumstances which initiated it have disappeared. Most authorities agree that stutterers account for from 1% to 2% of the school population and that they are more common among boys than girls.

Stuttering is basically due to lack of balance between the actions of the muscles of the mouth and throat. It is now generally believed that the mechanics of stuttering

[6] See page 175.
[7] These will be considered in the chapter dealing with physical defects —Chapter VII, page 157.

lie, not in the muscles themselves, but in the nervous system back of the muscles. When a child stutters, the muscles of speech production go into a sort of intermittent spasm which interrupts or inhibits the normal speech rhythm. Accompanying this phenomenon there is a general "tightening up" of the other muscles of the body, observed in contortions of the face and, occasionally, of other parts of the body. The "tightening up" of the muscles of the chest and diaphragm sometimes hampers the regular rhythm of breathing. With this muscular tension there is frequently an emotional disturbance. The emotional tension makes the stuttering worse; and thus a circle of reactions is set up. The stutterer begins to lose confidence in his ability to speak normally, is afraid of meeting strangers or people in authority, becomes self-conscious and embarrassed, and so develops feelings of self-pity and inferiority.

In certain situations, however, he can talk fairly well. For example, in the privacy of his own room, he can usually give long speeches without a trace of a stutter and can speak or sing in unison with other children without any difficulty. Such instances support the judgment that stuttering is basically a symptom of psychological or emotional disturbance.

Various Theories of Stuttering. Thorough medical and anatomical examination will usually reveal no defect of the organs of speech or of the nervous system sufficient in nature or extent to produce the disability. Of the various theories, other than medical and anatomical, that have been advanced to explain stuttering, we shall mention three: (1) the *educational theory,* which holds that stuttering is primarily a bad habit; (2) the *neurological theory,* which says that stuttering is caused by a lack of dominance of one cerebral hemisphere over the other, so that between the two there is continual conflict for the control of lower nerve centers; and (3) the *personality theory,* which suggests, as we have pointed out, that stuttering is caused by emotional factors. The first theory, which says that stuttering is a bad habit, does not add very much to our understanding of it. It is the two latter theories, therefore, that chiefly concern us.

The neurological view is especially interesting in the light of the newer ideas on "handedness," and we shall therefore elaborate briefly the concept of cerebral dominance in its relation to stuttering. It is an anatomical fact that the left cerebral hemisphere of the brain controls the motor activity of the right side of the body, and, vice versa, the right hemisphere controls the left side of the body. In right-handed people the left cerebral hemisphere is therefore said to be *dominant,* and in people who are *left-handed* the right cerebral hemisphere is dominant. By some authorities it is estimated that one third of all children are born left-handed.[8] Most parents view left-handedness with alarm, and start early to "correct" it. If it has not been corrected by the time the child gets to school, the teacher may plan a vigorous attack on the problem. With more or less difficulty, depending on the persistence of the condition, the "handedness" may be changed in certain activities (such as writing and eating). Hence, says the neurological theory, the right and left hemispheres conflict for dominance. The right is by nature dominant and the left is tending to become so by training. When the two reach a point of approximate equality, the theory contends, dominance

[8] This is by no means universally accepted. Many authorities would attribute handedness to incidental training after birth.

alternates, and this vacillating dominance is the essential cause of stuttering. In support of the theory, Travis [9] has demonstrated that among stuttering children changes in handedness have occurred with significant frequency.

Although the evidence remains inconclusive, it seems probable that, if a change of handedness is to be made, it should be made quietly, without forcing and, if possible, during the early preschool period. If the change cannot be accomplished without a great deal of trouble and emotional disturbance on the part of the child, it is better to leave well enough alone. Certainly if the child who has been "changed" starts to stutter, his old and natural handedness should be immediately encouraged. At such a time it makes no practical difference whether the cause is one of cerebral dominance or of emotional tension created by the effort to change a thoroughly ingrained motor habit.

Consideration of emotional tension as a cause of stuttering (the hypothesis of the "personality" theory) may be represented by example in a case history.

An eleven-year-old boy in Grade Six was referred to the psychologist because of an "impediment in his speech." The teacher's report stated that if he were asked a question suddenly, he would say two or three words and then block completely. His tongue seemed to catch behind his teeth. This resulted in a sort of stammer which was much more noticeable when he was excited. Such hurdles as oral tests in arithmetic were therefore very difficult for him. He was regarded as a good pupil in school, however, and a very conscientious worker. He had to repeat his first grade because of a change in schools, but had been promoted every year since. His mother explained that he had stammered since he was five years old.

[9] Travis, L. E., *Speech Pathology*, D. Appleton-Century Company, Inc., New York, 1931.

At that age he played with a little boy who stammered. He began to imitate this boy. In addition to his stammering it was discovered that he frequently was carsick and had dizzy spells. He was a sensitive lad, with a strong emotional attachment to his mother. The mother was a nervous woman. She had lost two babies before the boy was born, and was, therefore, somewhat overprotective of him. He was her only child. The father worked at night and left the mother and child alone in the house. The father was in poor health; and the family had been told to expect his death from heart disease at any time. Because both mother and son were afraid at night, they used to sleep together.

The boy was in good health. He had an I.Q. of 101. He seemed to be a serious sort of boy, but very friendly. He talked considerably and easily at the clinic. The special defect was interpreted as a symptom of his fear reaction, which in turn was due to complex factors—close mother-child relationship and the resulting overprotection of the child; lack of security; fear of father's sudden death, and so on. It was decided, therefore, that an effort should be made to work with the child rather than with his symptom. Various social and recreational activities (clubs, Y.M.C.A. camp, and so forth) were arranged to help develop his self-confidence and feelings of independence. The co-operation of his teacher was gained in an attempt to avoid those situations (for example, oral tests) that seemed to be causing him to stammer. Intensive speech training in a special class was not indicated at the time, nor was it ever required, as the stammering soon disappeared under the new activity regimen.

Helping the Stutterer. There are several ways in which the teacher can be helpful to the stuttering child:

1. Make sure of the child's general good health. Poor health habits or the presence of some chronic disease may have a part in causing or aggravating the condition.

2. Help the child to avoid violent emotional experiences such as temper tantrums and fear reactions. To discover the cause of the emotional difficulties, the whole diagnostic procedure is usually necessary.[10] Certain situations, problems, or disappointments may exist at home, at school, or in his personal life, which keep the child emotionally tense. While the teacher may not be able to do much regarding previously engendered emotional difficulties, he can help the pupil to face them frankly, rather than to regret or fear them.

3. Consider carefully the child's school life. School creates for the child many grave problems, among which oral responses before the class are most difficult. Usually it is best not to call on the stuttering child for oral work unless he volunteers to answer questions, to read, or to speak. If he does volunteer, the teacher should take care that, so far as possible, the attention of the class is not directed towards the child's defect. There should be no suggestion that the child's stuttering is due to the fact that "he is nervous," a comment that increases the child's consciousness of his defect. Under no circumstances should the child be treated with impatience, ridicule, or annoyance because of his handicap. Nor should he be treated with too much sympathy. Because of the child's stuttering, he may become shy and withdraw from social contacts. In a quiet way the teacher should encourage the child to participate in sports and other extracurricular activities.

4. Help the stutterer to develop his natural talents, improve his means of self-expression, and compensate for some of the restraint caused by a speech defect. Development of abilities such as those displayed in music, art, and hobbies reduces the feeling of inferiority that so often isolates the child from social contacts.

5. Try to encourage a candid attitude in the child toward his disability. The child should never be encouraged to feel that stuttering is something to be ashamed of, something to hide

[10] See Chapter IV.

from others. It is much better that he should stutter freely, accepting it as the natural way for his particular speech mechanism to function. If he does not mind his stuttering, almost no one else will.

6. Assist the child to form the best speech habits of which he is capable. With encouragement and support he can probably speak much better than he does. With the exception of the actual muscle spasm, the effort and straining that accompany his stuttering can largely be overcome. The effort to avoid stuttering before it occurs, and the effort to end stuttering as quickly as possible, are both bad habits which aggravate the condition. The child should learn to talk with no more effort than a normal speaker. Thus will he eliminate much of the strain, fatigue, and feeling of helplessness; and thus, also, will he keep the speech muscles at more nearly their normal tension, so that stuttering is less likely to occur.

When the teacher has followed all these suggestions, what next? Will the child outgrow his stuttering? Authorities believe that, in many cases, stuttering is a deep-rooted condition that demands a systematic treatment for its cure. When the teacher and the parents have done, without success, all they can do, they should consult a competent speech therapist. Modern science is attacking this handicap with increasing success. Competent specialists are becoming more numerous. More and more school systems are engaging the services of special teachers thoroughly trained in speech correction.

V. ENURESIS

Bladder control should be established at least by the time the child is three years of age. The condition in which there is lack of voluntary control, after the child has reached that age, is known as *enuresis*. The most frequent type of enuresis is bed-wetting; but some children have poor control even during the day. Enuresis is occasionally caused by certain physical disorders or by inadequate training. Usually, however, it is a symptom of poor emotional and personality development. Although physical disorder is a factor in only about 10% of the cases, a child with enuresis should be examined by a physician to make sure that any organic defects which may be present are properly treated.

Enuresis due to faulty habit formation is usually indicative of wrong attitudes on the part of parents. Some parents are careless and uninterested in child training; and some believe that the trouble is hereditary, and therefore they can do nothing about it. In certain homes the difficulty in training may be due to inadequate toilet facilities. In the case of border-line or mentally defective children, the learning of suitable habits may be a long process, and the parents may be unwilling to persevere in a tedious task. Sometimes the mother may excuse the child as being too small, too delicate, or too nervous—a type of excuse that betrays an unhealthy maternal attitude; the mother, unwilling that the child should grow up and achieve independence, welcomes enuresis as a sign that the child is still a baby and completely dependent on her.

More commonly, however, enuresis is a symptom of general emotional instability. Like stuttering, it is analogous to the nervous tic, which, beginning as a method of meeting frustration or avoiding difficulty, continues as a habit. It may be a means of securing attention, from which the child obtains satisfaction, not only in the concern and solicitation of his parents, but in the scoldings and punishments he receives. Sometimes it is an indirect method of taking revenge against parents, nurses, or teachers. The child may have some real or fancied spite against authority, and finds that this habit causes annoyance and embarrassment to his enemies. The mechanism, of course, is involuntary and unwitting. The child seldom wets deliberately.

When organic factors have been ruled out, and when careful attempts at habit training have no success, it is wise to make a careful study of the emotional satisfaction that the child is getting out of the practice. In most cases, this, again, is the task of the clinician.

A nine-year-old girl was referred to the psychiatrist because of "wetting." Her accidents occurred during and after school, as well as during the night. In addition to this symptom, she had "pains in her stomach," was a nervous child, a restless sleeper, and had bouts of weeping and temper. Her school record showed that although she was repeating Grade Two, she was doing good work. She had failed to pass her examinations the previous year because of poor reading ability. It was further ascertained that she was always more tense, nervous, irritable, and had more accidents when there was a test or examination in the offing. Her teacher insisted, however, that she caused no serious trouble except for her "weak kidneys." She played with other children in a normal way.

Though the girl was a pale, fair-haired child of slight build, she was quite healthy. Her I.Q. was 100. She lived at home with her mother, four brothers, and two sisters. The father had died suddenly and dramatically of heart failure six months previously. The child's enuresis began about that time.

A friendly discussion with the child revealed the fact that she had been particularly fond of her father; and his dramatic death, which the whole family witnessed, was a great shock to her. Her reading, always her chief difficulty at school, became much worse. Increasing nervousness and the approach of examinations at the close of the school year brought on her first accident. During the summer she was comparatively free from symptoms, but the thought of going back to school with the possibility of another humiliating accident or another failure was continually before her. When she did go back she tried resolutely but tensely to control herself. Because she was sensitive, she would not ask to leave the room.

Treatment consisted in helping her understand her own fears. She was put on her own responsibility to keep dry. It was arranged that she could leave the room whenever she wanted to without asking; and the teacher saw to it that she did go at least twice during each school session. The teacher became interested in the girl and her reading difficulty. Together they worked at her problems, and within a month the child's reading had greatly improved and enuresis had been overcome. (In this case, particularly, notice the supplementary effect of formal and traditional classroom procedure on personality development.)

When enuresis occurs in school, it is always humiliating for the child. The incident at school, however, is far from being the whole story. Many children who are bedwetters have the fact broadcast on the street and playground by older brothers or sisters; as a result they may be subjected to much cruel teasing, leading to a sense of unworthiness and feelings of inferiority. These children, then, may withdraw from social contacts and become seclusive, or may develop overcompensation such as bullying, fighting, and delinquency.

Treatment consists in helping the child face his difficulty and overcome it. Children of school age should shoulder a good portion of the responsibility. They should take it upon themselves to wake up during the night to use the toilet. If necessary they should use an alarm clock for this purpose. For the parent or teacher, the essential thing to keep in mind is that neither fear, shame, nor embarrassment should be employed to solve the problem. With the child's assistance it must be attacked by the teacher or parent in a thoroughly objective manner. They should be told that a perfect cure cannot be effected immediately, that relearning will, no doubt, be accompanied by occasional lapses, as in any other types of habit formation, but that careful attention to the problem will bring its reward.

VI. ANTISOCIAL TENDENCIES

Delinquency may be defined as activity that runs counter to the laws of the land, interfering with the rights or possessions of other persons. But in modern thought the definition does not brand the delinquent child as "criminal." Modern psychiatry is beginning to think of delinquency as but another symptom of faulty personality development; and the modern legal conception of delinquency places it under the civil law rather than the criminal. For example, the "Children's and Young Persons' Act" of 1933 in Great Britain lays down the principle that "every court in dealing with a child or young person brought before it shall have regard to the *welfare* of the child or young person." Actually, delinquency among children is an indication of inadequate guidance and guardianship, rather than a criminally perverted moral sense.

The most common delinquencies among school children are lying, stealing, destructiveness, truancy, and sex misdemeanors. Like stuttering, delinquency may become habitual, and, without any apparent reason, remain as an aspect of the child's behavior and personality. When we meet a boy who is set in delinquent ways, we think of him as a "bad boy"; but there is always a beginning of these antisocial trends; and the beginning is usually due to a well-defined cause or collection of causes. For this reason it is important to diagnose tendencies of this type early, before they have become chronic and while there is still a chance of eliminating the cause. Without a cause, the effect must disappear.

Lying. There are many degrees of lies and many reasons for lying. Some of them are serious; some of them are not. They vary from a simple exaggeration, which is one of the easiest ways of getting attention, to a deliberate untruth that is told in order to avoid punishment or gain advantage. Lying to avoid punishment has usually been preceded by another misdemeanor, such as stealing or truancy. To understand the lying, we must, therefore, look into the original misdemeanor and its underlying causes.

In building sound moral character, the influence of the home probably takes precedence over that of the school. It is in the home that the child is first exposed to forces that mold personality. There are parents, for instance, who are not too particular about their own truthfulness. Too often the child hears his parents excusing themselves from a tedious engagement with the plea that "visitors have just come," or that "a child is ill." Children of parents who habitually use false excuses are almost bound to develop untruthfulness.

Other parents unconsciously encourage false stories; they constitute themselves an indulgent "court of appeal" for every complaint which a child of theirs may make. If he is reprimanded at school for misbehavior they rush to his defense. They prefer to believe *his* word rather than that of his teacher or his principal; and they are all too prone to construct fantastic and exaggerated versions of what actually happened. Should the teacher and the principal prove reluctant to "admit their guilt," parents of this type are likely to appeal to the higher authority of the Board of Education, where, fortunately, they seldom obtain satisfaction. Such parents teach their offspring to escape, by falsification, the responsibility for his misbehavior.

In many cases of lying, the parents are less obviously at fault; in such instances the teacher is inclined to lay full responsibility on the child and exact punishment for the delinquency. Too often in schools the consequence of an untruth is corporal punishment, a form of treatment that has never yet cured a persistent liar. A more scientific attitude would be to try to understand the cause of the misbehavior, and if possible to remove it. Teachers who have learned to look for causes will almost always find, in these children, problems of emotional adjustment. But while looking for causes the teacher should never allow the child to escape responsibility for a serious lie. When he is quite sure that a lie has been told, he should talk quietly with the child and indicate clearly that he is not convinced. After all, lying represents logical, purposive behavior, and if the teacher can explain to the child the causes of his behavior and show him a more acceptable form of conduct, the child will see himself and his teacher with new eyes. No child resents frankness coupled with kindness; and frequently a talk of this kind begins a new and better relationship between teacher and pupil. Habits of truthfulness, by these means, naturally take their place, along with courtesy and kindness, among the forms of behavior that should be taken for granted in the classroom.

Stealing. Stealing, like lying, is often an indication of emotional maladjustment and frequently is the precursor of protective lying. A child may steal to gain prestige and attention by distributing his loot among his friends. By his bravado (and his bribes) he is able to gather about him a small group of admiring colleagues. Occasionally stealing is prompted by vindictiveness and jealousy: the child wishes to spite a more successful playmate. But most often children steal simply because they have nothing of their own. They take toys because other children have them and leave them around to be taken. The ethics of ownership seldom occurs to them. Later they take money for much the same reason. This sort of stealing is especially likely to occur if there are loose social standards at home. Often there is a real scramble for possessions among the children in such families, and "may the devil take the hindmost." Similar tendencies are but a little below the surface in some adults who are no more honest than the law demands.

A twelve-year-old boy in the auxiliary class of a large school had been staying out late at night, stealing, and lying. The distraught parents were referred to the clinic by the principal. A complete history showed that his school progress had always been unsatisfactory. He had spent three years in Grade One and two in Grade Two. After five years, he was discouraged, sulky, and disobedient. He was sent to the auxiliary class for individual teaching in order to "get him started properly." In the auxiliary class his conduct was described as "poor." He was overactive, restless, and resentful of authority. Nevertheless, he was a leader in his class. He showed extreme emotional variability. Sometimes he was gloomy and irritable, at other times good-natured and cheerful. He loved to "act the fool" behind the teacher's back in order to make the others laugh, and was punished several times for this behavior. At home there were difficulties. The mother claimed her nerves were bad, and the father was said to be impatient and bad-tempered. There was no consistent routine, and the discipline was inadequate. The boy was punished severely at home whenever he was caught in disobedience or misdemeanor.

An interview with the boy showed him to be a large healthy fellow. He was well mannered and pleasant. His I.Q. was 86. In confidence, he explained with considerable feeling that he hated school, hated his home, and hated everybody. Other boys did not like him and called him "big feet." He was clumsy at games and sports. He felt very inferior in many ways. One way to gain some attention and recognition was to cause a fuss at school and to make the other children laugh. Another way was to exhibit his prowess at stealing and his defiance of authority in staying out late.

Treatment was directed to the cause of the trouble. Constructive social and school programs were drawn up, involving transfer to a nonacademic school for adolescent boys and membership in the Scouts. He is being given further guidance as required. The prognosis, however, must be guarded.

In the treatment of these children, the question we must answer is not how to punish the thief, but why did he steal? To get to the root of the trouble, complete diagnostic procedures are usually necessary.[11] *Esprit de corps* in a class will do much to prevent stealing and lying, but if children persist in stealing or in antisocial behavior of an even more serious character, there is no alternative but to seek the help of specialists in juvenile delinquency. Institutional treatment in an industrial school of some sort may be indicated for certain children. Such treatment, however, is usually considered an admission of failure on the part of the home and the

[11] See Chapter IV.

school in their attempt to meet the needs of the developing child.

Sex Misdemeanors. Sexual behavior of any kind in and around the school is likely to be regarded as a sign of delinquency. Sometimes it is, indeed, a manifestation of serious psychological illness. Because of deeply ingrained social attitudes and taboos, such misdemeanors are regarded with particular disapproval by adults. Included in this category are such things as smutty talk, drawing suggestive pictures on the walls, masturbation (self-abuse), and the more serious and perverted forms of antisocial sexual behavior. Occasionally children who are mentally retarded have precocious sexual development and may molest other children. These must be intelligently understood and carefully managed. For the protection of others, they may have to be removed from the group.

Often, as far as the child is concerned, sex misbehavior is not consciously sexual at all. It is fascinating to the child merely because it is recognized as being so very "bad." Many psychiatrists think that the superficial type of sexual behavior has a certain educational value. They argue that if the child is not exposed to sex influences, he may develop an artificial and even erroneous conception of sex. The disillusionment that eventually follows may be devastating in its effect on personality. It is obvious that this point of view assumes a lack or failure of sex training at home. Without condoning it, however, it is true that one may pay far too much attention to mild forms of sex behavior. The teacher who is unduly sensitive, and always on the watch for the slightest indication of sex activity, may develop in his pupils attitudes and interests that are definitely more harmful than those that might have occurred if the teacher had completely ignored the matter. When smutty talk occurs among a group of children of the same sex, it should be overlooked, if possible. Usually the attention of the group can be quickly and effectively directed into more useful channels that are equally interesting. However, when such talk is annoying or embarrassing to unwilling listeners, interference is justified. Smutty and vulgar scribbling on the walls can be erased after school hours without comment and without attracting any attention. If an attempt is made to find the culprit, the result will be not only embarrassing to the teacher, but of doubtful value to the children.

Masturbation in class is occasionally encountered. Sometimes an immature or retarded child, not realizing the nature of the behavior, is encouraged in the act by other children; sometimes an older child uses masturbation to attract the attention of fellow pupils—really a form of compensation. This, again, is a situation that is embarrassing to the teacher. Its prevention is always easier than its cure. A child who is busy working at something in which he is interested will not offend in this way. No matter how immature or retarded a child may be, there is always something to be found that will interest him. Once the offense has occurred, it should be dealt with in precisely the same manner as a temper tantrum. The child should be banished as quickly and quietly as possible. The subsequent investigation must be directed towards an intelligent understanding of the whole episode, not only by the teacher but by the child.

The attitude of the children in the class to such misdemeanors will depend on their ages and on the amount of sex education they have had. Owing to the present state of public opinion, it is wise to err on the conservative side in the matter of sex education in school. Pupils in the senior grades will learn much, by inference, from the study of biology and zoology, even though the problems of plant and animal reproduction are treated (as they should be) purely objectively and perhaps somewhat guardedly. It may indeed be argued that children will not learn enough of the facts of human procreation by this process. Nevertheless, it is unwise to go further in the classroom. Some parents are certain to be outraged; and, as a result, the overzealous but well-meaning teacher may find himself an object of suspicion, if not attack. Sex education, in the narrow sense, remains, by popular approval, the special task of the parents or the family doctor.

VII. POOR PROGRESS IN SCHOOL

Uneven or retarded progress through school is a problem that interests every teacher. Few teachers, however, recognize the relation between this and the more general problem of personality development. There are so many ways in which a child may fail in school. In one sense, all the difficulties described in the earlier sections of this chapter represent school failures, but at this point we are concerned particularly with the child who, for one reason or another, is unable to make the progress in academic work that is normally expected of him. Instead of emotional instability or any of the other manifestations of stunted or thwarted development, the chief, and sometimes the only, symptom may be school failure. If energies are being used up in a fruitless attempt to satisfy needs or meet impossible requirements, there may be none left to spend on schoolwork. And so the child falls behind. His failure may be a general one all along the line or may be limited to one or two specific subjects.

In case of school failure, it is quite useless to scold or threaten, or even to coax the child to do better. The problem does not lie in the schoolwork itself or the child's application to it. It may have no relation to the child's intelligence or even to his previous training. The problem is much deeper than that. A satisfactory solution will depend on a careful appraisal of all the factors at home or at school that are influencing the child. The difficulty may be in the child's poor physical health, or, as is more likely to be the case, in the child's poor emotional and social development.

As well as being a symptom of poor development, school failure is frequently a cause of it. In such a case, school failure is usually related directly to poor intelligence, poor health, or inadequate preparation. It reflects one of the impossible requirements that the child's environment makes upon him, and sets the stage so that it is difficult for the child to satisfy many of his basic personality needs. The result, as we have seen, is stunted or warped personality development.

VIII. SOME CONCLUSIONS

The teacher will have realized by now that the important thing about understanding children is not the problems they happen to have. It makes little difference whether poor personality development takes the form of stuttering or bullying. These, like headaches, are only symptoms. The important point to remember is that the symptoms are indications of a background of many factors and forces, each exerting some influence in molding the developing personality.

REFERENCES

The following references have been arranged according to the problems covered in this chapter. They will serve as starting points for the teachers who wish to do more intensive reading in these and related fields.

I. Emotional Maladjustment

Arlitt, A. H., *Adolescent Psychology*, American Book Company, New York, 1933

Brooks, F. D., and Shaffer, L. F., *Child Psychology*, Houghton Mifflin Company, Boston, 1937 (See Chapter X.)

Hart, B., *The Psychology of Insanity*, The Macmillan Company, New York, 1931

Louttit, C. M., *Clinical Psychology*, Harper and Brothers, New York; The Musson Book Company, Toronto, 1936 (See Chapters VIII, IX, and XII.)

Martens, E. H., and Russ, H., *The Adjustment of Behavior Problems of School Children*, United States Office of Education, Bulletin No. 18, Washington, D. C., Government Printing Office, 1932

"Mental Hygiene and Adjustment," *Review of Educational Research*, VI:5, December, 1936

Morgan, J. J. B., *The Psychology of the Unadjusted School Child* (Revised), The Macmillan Company, New York, 1936

Rivlin, H. N., *Educating for Adjustment*, D. Appleton-Century Company, Inc., New York, 1936

Shaffer, L. F., *The Psychology of Adjustment*, Houghton Mifflin Company, Boston, 1936

Sherman, M., *Mental Hygiene and Education*, Longmans, Green & Co., New York, 1934

Symonds, P. M., *The Mental Hygiene of the School Child*, The Macmillan Company, New York, 1934

II. Nervousness

Cameron, H. C., *The Nervous Child* (Fourth Edition), Oxford University Press, New York, 1929

Terman, L. M., and Almack, J. C., *The Hygiene of the School Child* (Revised), Houghton Mifflin Company, Boston, 1929 (See Chapters XV and XVII.)

III. Stuttering

Blanton, M. G., and Blanton, S., *Speech Training for Children,* D. Appleton-Century Company, Inc., New York, 1919

Boome, E. J., and Richardson, M. A., *The Nature and Treatment of Stammering,* E. P. Dutton & Co., Inc., 1932

Fletcher, J. M., *The Problem of Stuttering,* Longmans, Green & Co., New York, 1928

McAllister, A. H., *Clinical Studies in Speech Therapy,* University of London Press, Ltd., London, 1937

Seth, G., and Guthrie, D. J., *Speech in Childhood,* Oxford University Press, New York, 1935

See also the references given in Chapter VII, page 177.

IV. Problems of Habit Training

Blatz, W. E., and Bott, H., *Parents and the Pre-school Child,* William Morrow & Company, Inc., New York; J. M. Dent & Sons, Ltd., Toronto, 1929

Child Management, United States Department of Labor, Children's Bureau, Publication No. 143, Government Printing Office, Washington, D. C., 1937

Good Habits for Children, Metropolitan Life Insurance Company, New York and Ottawa

The Child from One to Six, United States Department of Labor, Children's Bureau, Publication No. 30, Government Printing Office, Washington, D. C., 1935

Thom, D. A., *Everyday Problems of the Everyday Child*, D. Appleton-Century Company, Inc., New York, 1927 (See Chapter VI.)

V. Delinquency

Burt, C. L., *The Young Delinquent* (Third Revised Edition), University of London Press, Ltd., London, 1938

Hartwell, Samuel, *Fifty-five Bad Boys*, Alfred A. Knopf, Inc., New York, 1931

Healy, W., and others, *Reconstructing Behavior in Youth*, Alfred A. Knopf, Inc., New York, 1929

VI. General References

Groves, E. R., and Blanchard, P. M., *Introduction to Mental Hygiene*, Henry Holt and Company, Inc., 1930

Kanner, Leo, *Child Psychiatry*, Charles C. Thomas, Publisher, Springfield, 1935

Louttit, C. M., *Clinical Psychology*, Harper & Brothers, New York; The Musson Book Company, Ltd., Toronto, 1936 (See Part III.)

Sayles, M. B., *The Problem Child in School*, Joint Committee on Methods of Preventing Delinquency, New York, 1925

Sex Education—Symposium for Educators, United States Office of Education, V. D. Pamphlet No. 86, Government Printing Office, Washington, D. C., 1927 (See also V. D. Pamphlet No. 7.)

CHAPTER IV

THE DIAGNOSTIC APPROACH TO CLASSROOM PROBLEMS

I. THE DIAGNOSTIC POINT OF VIEW

We have assumed that education is vitally interested in the development of children—especially in the healthy development of their personalities. The work of education as a social enterprise is thus analogous to the promotion of sound physical health in the community by the Department of Public Health. The physicians in such a department are continually striving to improve the living conditions of the people. For the prevention of disease they give the widest publicity to the need for such positive factors as good food, intelligent exercise, adequate sanitation, inoculation, and vaccination, and these desirable ends are often supported by legislation. One of the principles of health that receives widest publicity is the early and adequate diagnosis of disease, for disease may be treated most successfully when it is discovered early, before serious and permanent damage has been done. The same principle may be applied to the functions of mind and personality. Disorders of personality, observed in childhood, diagnosed and treated in time, are absolutely amenable not only to control but to correction. This chapter deals with a simple method for the diagnosis of those disorders of personality which the teacher may encounter in the classroom. Although he may not be a professional psychiatrist or psychologist, a teacher can systematically collect information that will help him solve most of his educational problems, in so far as they refer to the personalities of his pupils.

85

When confronted with a problem of disease, the physician has in mind certain definite procedures that he follows almost automatically. In the first place, he "takes a history." He listens to the patient's description of the complaint and asks pertinent questions about the onset of the trouble, the patient's past health, and the functioning of the various organs of the body. He then proceeds to make his "physical examination." He inspects the whole body carefully, looks into the mouth, listens through his stethoscope to the action of the heart and lungs, and goes through other routine procedures, testing out each function in turn. Finally he may complete his examination by the use of several specialized tests such as the chemical analysis of the urine, the microscopic appearance of the blood, and X-ray photographs.

The teacher will find it useful to have some similar orderly procedure in dealing with classroom problems. Much of the information that he needs is already at hand. Classroom and school records as well as the record of examinations made by the school physician furnish an excellent start. Some of the necessary information the teacher can collect only by consultation with the parents; and the most important details of the data will have to be obtained through special procedures involving the child himself.

II. COLLECTING AND RECORDING INFORMATION

Although it is an excellent exercise in diagnostic procedure to write out all the significant details of a specific case under an orderly arrangement of headings,[1] the teacher should remember that collecting and recording the information is not important in itself. Information is

---

[1] A suitable outline for such a report is appended; see page 109.

only important in so far as it can be put to use at once for the child's benefit. Some educational authorities supply special forms and blanks to be filled in by the teacher, either as a routine procedure for every child or for the purpose of reporting the "problem child." These are likely to be stereotyped; and often, after all the blank spaces have been checked or filled in, the teacher has indicated but a minimum of significant and useful information. It is much better, with the data collected, to write simple descriptive accounts of the case in a manner thoroughly objective. The most important thing for the teacher to remember is the necessity of discriminating between "facts" as he knows them and "facts" reported by other people. In addition the teacher must not record as factual material that which is merely his own opinion or interpretation. A diagnosis or an interpretation of the child's behavior should be reserved until all the facts are at hand and can be critically analyzed.

Frequently a child who creates no particular problem in the classroom is nevertheless in trouble on account of his behavior at home or elsewhere. In this case the teacher is often requested to furnish a report of the child's progress and behavior at school. This should follow the same general headings as the more complete report, except that it is not necessary to include information on such topics as background, development, home, and parents. These details of the "history" will usually have been covered by the agency requesting the school report.

III. INFORMATION FROM THE SCHOOL RECORDS

There is a wealth of important information obtainable from the ordinary cumulative record card which is usually kept for each pupil. If this card has been kept up to date, it will contain such data as the following:

Birth date
Age on entering school
Number of days (or terms) spent in each grade (Grades repeated)
Number of days absent or late
Pupil's achievement record in each grade and, usually, in each subject
Frequency with which the pupil has changed schools

The value of this information is obvious. Often children are not allowed to go to school until they reach the age when they are legally required to go. In a lock-step system, a child's late entrance may mean that he begins school a year or so late and is continually behind others of his own age through no fault of his own. Similarly, poor attendance in the early years may explain poor ability in the fundamental subjects. On the other hand, one frequently has to deal with a child who, in spite of an excellent past record, begins suddenly to fall behind. This frequently indicates the presence of some emotional difficulty which the teacher may be able to alleviate or remove.

The record usually contains also a report of examinations made by the school physician at specific times during the elementary-school career. Children with physical defects require special care and, usually, special educational procedures. If a child who is having some difficulty in getting along well in school has not had a thorough physical examination for some time or does not appear to be physically healthy, the teacher should arrange for him to be examined as soon as possible. It is not uncommon to meet cases where defective vision has passed unnoticed for years and has been responsible for poor reading, poor spelling, and general retardation. The child who is slightly deaf may present a serious educational problem, and his deafness may not have been discovered by a succession of teachers. Chronic infection from diseased tonsils or other sources may have an important bearing on a child's general health and behavior. Many of the educational problems arising from such physical disabilities will be fully considered in the following chapters.[2]

The teacher in remote areas, where no medical or nursing assistance can be obtained, may be compelled to do some amateur examining himself.[3] There is much that the observant teacher can do on his own initiative. The height and weight of the pupils can certainly be measured and compared with tables published in health reference books.[4] These tables, however, quickly become obsolete and, in fact, since they refer to an average, may be quite misleading when applied to an individual. Stress is now being placed by health authorities on an adequate annual increase in height and weight, rather than on mere conformity to expectancy tables. Poor posture in sitting and standing is often significant as an indication of poor health or poor health habits.[5] The examination of the nose and throat for obvious defects and signs of disease is important. An estimate of the extent of any visual or

[2] See especially Chapter VII.

[3] Many texts on health and health education contain detailed instructions on how to make a quick health survey of children. See, for example, *The Hygiene of the School Child* by Terman and Almack. See also the references at the end of this chapter.

[4] Weight-height-age tables for boys and girls can be purchased for a few cents from the United States Office of Education, Washington, D. C.

[5] See, for instance, R. E. Grout's *Handbook of Health Education* (Doubleday, Doran and Company, Inc., New York, 1936).

auditory defects can be quickly made by one of several easy methods.[6]

Although there is no doubt that there are thousands of physically defective children in our schools, it may be comforting to teachers to know that the great majority of children are either healthy and normal in every way or suffering from physical defects which are easily recognized. A recent report of a school health survey in Saskatchewan, for example, showed that in over 15,000 pupils 28% were normal, 22% had diseased tonsils, 14% were underweight, 13% had poor vision, and 1% had defects of hearing.[7] These categories alone accounted for over 75% of the children examined. The types of defect included in this list were so obvious that most of them could have been recognized by any interested teacher.

The cumulative school record will contain also information concerning any psychological tests that have been administered in the past. In each case it is important to note the nature of the test, the date it was given, and the result. It will be useful to compare the results of former tests with the result of subsequent psychological examinations.

IV. CLASSROOM BEHAVIOR

The first part of the report can be completed by a written description of the chief characteristics of the child as observed in classroom situations. Such a statement should include the teacher's evaluation of the child's schoolwork, with reference to special abilities or disabili-

---

[6] Rough tests for these defects are described in Chapter VII (pages 161 through 167). They will be found also in any good handbook on health (see the references at the end of this chapter).

[7] Binning, G., "Adequate School Examination," *Canadian Public Health Journal*, 29, I, January, 1938, pages 13-18.

ties in classroom performance. It should also include a short description of the child's general appearance. What does he look like? Is he usually clean, neat, and tidy, or is he slovenly and dirty in his dress and habits? Is he overactive, restless, talkative, and impulsive, or slow, quiet, and lethargic? Has he normal self-control? Does he have any nervous habits such as nail biting or blinking? What are the qualities of his speech? Are there any special defects or indications of the influence of a foreign language? What is the character of his conversation?

Without reference to psychological tests, the teacher should estimate the level of the child's intellectual development.

What are his habits and methods of work? Can he pay attention and concentrate successfully on one thing at a time? Has he good manual dexterity? Has the child displayed any particular interest in intellectual, artistic, or practical pursuits?

In a similar manner, his social and emotional development should be briefly described. Who are his friends? Are they younger or older than he? Is he a sociable child or does he tend to be solitary? Is he shy in school, or forward? daydreaming or matter-of-fact? How does he play with others? Does he always want to be boss, or does he usually allow himself to be led and influenced by others? Is he polite, obedient, honest, kindly, and generous, or the reverse? Has he any particular social interests such as the Boy Scouts, clubs, or societies? Has the child normal emotional stability, or does he cry on the slightest provocation? Has he any obvious fears and worries? What is his characteristic mood—cheerful or gloomy? good-natured or irritable? Is he unusually sensitive, easily discouraged or depressed? Has he any feelings of inferiority? Is he unduly aggressive? jealous? Does he bully the younger children? hold grudges? resent authority? All these questions have reference to the kind of behavior and the personality development that can be expected normally at the child's particular age level. In this connection the teacher is referred to the norms of personality development listed in Chapter II.[8]

When the request for information on the child has come from an outside agency, the teacher's report ends here. If he is interested in developing a full report for his own use, there is still much important information to be obtained.

V. INFORMATION FROM THE PARENTS

An accurate and detailed account of the child's family environment can best be obtained by having an experienced social worker or school nurse visit the home. There is much significant information, however, that the teacher himself may obtain from an informal talk with the mother. Such a visit is a time-consuming task often regarded as one of the teacher's trials in life; but when the interview is skillfully guided it is not without compensation. Often it opens the way to a complete understanding and solution of the problem.

There are certain key facts that should be known about the child's background. His position in the family with respect to the brothers and sisters, if not indicated on the school records, should be determined. If one or both parents are dead, or if they are separated, a note to the effect should be included. Some estimate of the social status and material condition of the home can usually be made in the course of the general conversa-

[8] See page 11.

tion. It is important, for instance, to know what facilities are provided for sleeping and recreation. But more important are the personalities of the parents and their attitude toward the child and his problem. An over-ambitious mother or an overcritical father frequently contributes to the child's difficulty. Without seeming to appear too inquisitive or critical the teacher can usually find out how the parents regard the child's ability, his social and emotional adjustments, and how they have managed discipline at home.

Any special circumstance in the home environment that is likely to have an influence on the child's development should be recorded. Such factors as the presence of a more successful or more favored brother or sister, extremely stern disciplinary measures, and bad examples set by other members of the family in terms of peculiar social attitudes or faulty moral behavior are cases in point. This sort of information seldom comes out spontaneously in an interview but frequently is brought to the attention of the teacher through other means.

It is useful to have some information about the child's early development. Detailed accounts of the birth, age of teething, talking, and walking are sometimes of interest, but on the whole are better left to the specialist. Feeble-minded children as a rule develop slowly in these respects; but so do many normal and even superior children. It is much more significant to discuss with the parent any serious illness through which the child has passed. Particularly important are dramatic crises such as pneumonia, convulsions, major operations, and accidents. The effect of these on the personality of both the child and the mother is often quite marked. Parents tend to coddle or to be oversympathetic and overprotective to children who have suffered in this manner; and the children, in turn, tend to develop more than their share of self-pity.

Experience in psychological clinics for children shows that many of the problems arising in the home have to do with poor habits of eating, sleeping, elimination, and sex. If there is trouble in connection with any of these habits the parent will usually hasten to tell the sympathetic teacher all about it. It is wise to refer the parent in these cases to the specialist or to the clinic for help. When there are no clinical facilities available, the teacher is often called upon to give advice himself. Occasionally problems related to faulty personal habits carry over into the classroom and become therefore the concern of the teacher.[9]

VI. INFORMATION FROM THE CHILD

The Personal Interview. The teacher will wish to become acquainted as fully as possible with the child himself. One of the best ways of developing acquaintance is by means of a friendly personal talk. If this technique is used, it must not take the form of an inquisition, a lecture, or a scolding. The prime necessities are sincerity, good will, and respect for the personality of the child. In such a frank discussion, all animosity and blame should be eliminated; the confidence of the child must be secured; and the teacher must be worthy of that confidence and respect it. If children do not trust adults, it is because bitter experience has taught them not to do so. Their tenderest feelings are often made the subject of laughter and ridicule; and their most cherished confi-

---

[9] For further information on the handling of problems in habit training, the teacher is referred to the sources mentioned on pages 83 and 84.

dences are broadcast in a manner that adults would not dare to use with one another.

In the discussion, at which no third person should be present, the child's interests can be explored. Conversation can be directed to the things he likes to do and the things he finds difficult, his loves and hates, his activities in school as well as outside. Are his interests mechanical, artistic, or athletic? Does he enjoy solitary pastimes more than group activities? Conversation on these topics may lead to the disclosure of an interest which the teacher never suspected before, and may serve as a starting point for the teacher's attack on the problem. Such an interest becomes invaluable when plans for the future are being made, for in this area at least the child is emotionally keen, and his enthusiastic co-operation can be secured.

In such an interview, the teacher should be careful to discuss seriously any question which the child raises. Explanations should be given, if possible. If the explanation or answer to a child's question involves a discussion of material which is emotionally painful for the child, or socially unacceptable for the teacher, indirect or partial answers can be given without straying from the truth.

Conversation with the child about his home and members of his family often reveals strange antagonisms and sometimes serious jealousies, feelings that may be unsuspected by the family, yet may often form the very root of the problem under consideration.

The child's attitude to his school and teacher is quite as important as his attitude to his family. The teacher will seldom learn directly the child's attitude toward the school and the teacher, but often he will be aware of distrust and antagonism. Antagonism toward the school should not call forth an answering antagonism in the teacher. Rather he should ask himself why he has failed to win the child's confidence, respect, and good will. If the class is to be a co-operative group, he must win the co-operation of every member. As a matter of fact, it is dangerous for the teacher to allow himself to dislike a pupil. Sometimes it is difficult to be fond of a child who is constantly causing trouble, but once the teacher allows himself to dislike the child, it is practically impossible for him to do much in the way of helping him. Indeed it happens not infrequently that the teacher first develops an unreasonable antagonism toward a child who responds, naturally enough, by disliking the teacher. The teacher then becomes bait for the child's animosity, and, mutually, pupil and teacher become "problems" to each other. In such a case there is little chance that the teacher can be of assistance in the personal difficulties of his pupil. Only by liking his pupils and by being objectively interested in all of them can the teacher hope to win their friendship and confidence. The interview should not close before a few plans have been discussed and accepted. The plans should not necessarily deal with the underlying difficulties as discussed in the interview. The teacher must make sure that the conversation ends on a cheerful and encouraging note.

Intelligence Tests. The results of a carefully administered intelligence test aid materially in making a diagnosis. Intelligence tests aim to determine the general mental caliber or educability of a child at a given age level, relative to all other children of his age. Their construction is highly technical and is the work of the psychological specialist. The teacher, however, should know something about the work of Alfred Binet, who, in collaboration with Dr. Simon, constructed a standardized scale for indicating the likelihood of success in school-work, and the general scope of later extensions of Binet's research.

Intelligence tests are either (*a*) of the *individual* type —by which one child is examined at a time, in private; or (*b*) of the *group* type—by which a number of children are examined at the same time, as in a written examination. Tests of the individual type are more reliable for appraising a child's general intellectual caliber. Their administration demands that the examiner be carefully trained in the theory and procedures involved.

For general purposes, the individual test most generally used is the Stanford Revision of the *Binet-Simon Test*. A new revision of this test has recently been published and is gradually replacing the older scale.

Certain children have considerable difficulty with the Binet and similar tests because of the "language ability" required. English may not be spoken at home, for instance. Some of these children may be more easily compared with the group by means of a "non-language" or "performance" type of test.[10] Again, such tests require administration by a specialist.

Group tests may be administered by classroom teachers who will take pains to become familiar with the directions (published in the manual for any given test) and who will follow those directions in a thoroughly scientific way. Most group tests involve careful attention to time limits; and all of them demand that the instructions-for-administering be followed with strict attention to detail. The results of group tests are usually reliable with refer-

[10] A short but carefully compiled list of suitable intelligence tests, individual and group, is appended to this chapter (page 107). Publishers and costs are indicated.

ence to the whole group tested. They may be quite unreliable, however, in a particular case. Bright children, for instance, tend to have scores on group tests somewhat lower than the scores on individual tests; dull pupils often get scores higher than those obtained with the more accurate techniques. An individual's group-test score may be lowered by accidental circumstances (such as a broken pencil, an unfortunate position in the classroom) which cannot be corrected during the examination.

The nature of "intelligence"—or what is measured by the tests—is essentially a psychological matter. Functionally, it refers to one's ability to see relationships among phenomena. The more intelligent child sees relationships more quickly, can comprehend more complex relational structures, and usually sees more pertinent relationships in any given situation. He can also apply his relationships (such as abstract scientific principles, for example) more freely and easily to new situations. Tests of intelligence seem to give measures that are consistent from test to test, despite the wide variety of forms that different tests assume. They, therefore, may be said to indicate an important, broad aspect of ability. They are usually scored in a way that makes age comparisons among children possible. Hence the concept "mental age," which indicates broadly the degree of general intellectual maturity a child has achieved to date. This general intellectual growth, which, in this sense, appears to depend very little on training, progresses fairly evenly until early adolescence, and apparently ceases at about the age of fourteen to sixteen. An individual's rate of general intellectual growth (Intelligence Quotient, or I.Q.) is estimated by comparing his "Mental Age" with his "Chronological Age." For convenience, the formula

$IQ = \dfrac{MA}{CA} \times 100$ is universally used; but for children of sixteen years and over (chronologically) the divisor (CA) is never taken as greater than sixteen. Theoretically, the I.Q. remains constant throughout life. A good deal of controversy, however, still exists on this point.[11]

This factor in personality, the general intellectual caliber, represents an index of the individual's potentiality for development. Like many other measurable individual differences (height, weight, musical talent, and so forth), it is assumed to be distributed *normally* in the population at large. Normal distribution of intelligence means that there are relatively few people extremely high or extremely low; most people show degrees of intelligence that are fairly close to the average. In other words, if we plotted the intelligence of a representative sample of the population, the distribution would be similar to that shown in the figure below:

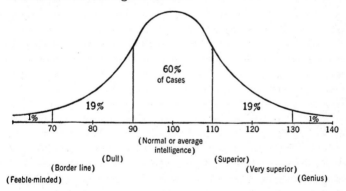

The scale is to be thought of as continuous, and the categories (feeble-mindedness, border line, and so on) are not to be taken as arbitrary classifications. We shall have occasion to refer to this distribution of intelligence

[11] See page 15.

again, in connection with the chapters dealing with special problems.[12]

While a careful use of intelligence-test results can be of great assistance to the educator in understanding his pupils, there are certain difficulties and dangers in their application. The quantitative result of these intelligence tests, in terms of a number purporting to signify the mental age or the intelligence quotient, is often given exaggerated importance. It almost seems as if some satisfaction were gained by labeling different children with different numbers. Particularly is this true of those children who have been causing trouble or who have been doing poorly in schoolwork and who have obtained low scores on the tests. Test results, therefore, must be viewed in perspective. There are many reasons why the actual score or number obtained is the least valuable part of the whole procedure. An experienced examiner takes notice of many things during the test, such as the child's attitude and reaction to the test situation, his special abilities and disabilities as revealed by the test, and his emotional and personality characteristics. These qualitative aspects of the formal intelligence test can never be indicated by a number or a score. They may seriously affect the score, however, and, unless given careful consideration, may lead to a definitely wrong impression of the child's general ability.

It should always be recognized and remembered that a quantitative estimate of the child's general intelligence is *only for the private use of the teacher or educator.* The child should learn to know his own capacity by what he does and can do—not as a number representing Mental Age or I.Q. The parent may, on occasion, have to be

[12] See Chapters V and VI.

consulted if the school authorities realize that the parental aspirations or demands in regard to the child's achievements are too great or too small. But then, as a rule, frank indication, in an atmosphere of friendly and co-operative discussion, can bring the parents to understand that much can be expected from the child, or that his progress will necessarily be slower than was anticipated —without any bandying of technical, and especially quantitative, terms. A great deal of misunderstanding and misconception can arise if a precipitate and unwise use of the I.Q. concept enters into the situation.

Educational Tests. In addition to tests of intelligence, there are many tests which have been devised in order to assess the child's progress in schoolwork. These *educational tests* are of two kinds: (1) *achievement tests,* which are designed to measure the extent of the child's knowledge in school subjects; and (2) *diagnostic tests,* which are used for determining the nature and extent of fundamental difficulties in certain subjects. Achievement tests, as would be expected, are based mainly on the notion that, at a certain age and grade level, school children should know a certain number of specified facts. They have been used extensively in connection with the problem of placing a new pupil in his proper grade or of measuring the progress made by a whole class over a period of months. They are usually constructed from the point of view of "content" and, therefore, must of necessity vary from place to place, depending on the curriculum requirements. It is the opinion of the writers that such tests have a limited value. Some teachers are completely unnerved and demoralized by the placing of too much emphasis on the importance of such tests as measurements of class progress and teaching efficiency. In many instances, bad effects on the children themselves have been observed, especially on those children who had tendencies toward emotional and nervous instability. In most cases the correct grade placement of a child can be efficiently determined by placing him with his age group and observing his attempts at adjustment. In the few cases in which good adjustments are not made, the difficulty is usually one of limited general intellectual ability. Such children should be placed according to their *mental* ages. In some cases, educational acceleration will complicate the picture, but the alert teacher will quickly diagnose the difficulty and make the necessary changes.[13]

Diagnostic tests, while subject to the same criticism, may be more useful to the teacher. The problem of special subject disability has received a considerable amount of attention by educationists and psychologists. The various types of special difficulties have been analyzed, and tests have been devised to show their nature and extent. In spite of all this research, current opinion suggests that a "special disability" should be regarded as an indication of inadequacies in the educational program, or as an aspect of the child's emotional adjustment, or both. The subjects usually giving the most difficulty in this regard are reading and arithmetic.

In diagnosing the problem in children with "special disability," such obvious factors as limited intelligence and physical defect must first be ruled out. A few simple diagnostic tests [14] may be useful in helping the teacher assess the nature and the extent of the disability.

[13] The problem of grading and placing is discussed more fully in Chapter IX.

[14] Complete lists of diagnostic tests will be found in many of the books listed at the end of the chapter. (See particularly the references listed under (c) *Educational Factors*.) A few of those most easily used by teachers are listed on pages 108 and 109.

Occasionally the difficulty can be traced to an emotional "blind spot" which the child has developed for a certain subject. There does not seem to be any specific disability underlying the failure, apart from the child's conviction that he cannot succeed. The reason may go back to early difficulties and failures which, while trivial in the eyes of the teacher, may have been overwhelming to the child. The recurring thought of these difficulties, combined with the oft-repeated admission on the part of the child's parents, his teacher, and himself, that he has a special disability, leaves the child convinced that he is inferior in ability at the given activity. This attitude, nurtured and developed over a period of several years, is extremely difficult to overcome. Several approaches are available. The teacher can start with the fundamentals and first principles of a subject, trying to build up the child's self-confidence by making sure that no mention is made of failure or special disability. A more indirect approach, however, may be more successful. Confidence must be combined with interest and incentive. If a child wants a thing badly enough he is likely to try very hard to obtain it. In other words, it is a problem in *motivation.* But it is not a question of motivating the child so that he learns something that we think he should. It is a question of kindling in him an interest so that the feared subject begins to emerge in a new light with new meanings for him. The subject in this new light has none of the old bogies attached to it. It is no longer feared, because it can be used daily in his own world.

VII. THE ART OF DIAGNOSIS

The methods of securing information, suggested in the foregoing pages, should result not merely in a mass of unrelated data, but rather in a unified picture of a living person. Diagnosis requires the gathering together of data from many sources. Correlating the data and interpreting their meaning come with experience and constitute an art that every teacher should cultivate.

This art is primarily based on an understanding of children individually. No universal rules of interpretation and treatment can be given. Every child is unique, and his problems must be understood in the light of the many factors influencing his development. Some of the most frequently encountered problems and suitable remedial measures are discussed in succeeding chapters.

REFERENCES

Descriptions of diagnostic procedures useful in determining the relative importance of physical, mental, and environmental factors in children with problems will be found in the following references:

(a) General References

> Bassett, Clara, *The School and Mental Health,* The Commonwealth Fund, New York, 1931
>
> Louttit, C. M., *Clinical Psychology,* Harper and Brothers, New York; The Musson Book Company, Ltd., Toronto, 1936 (See Part I.)
>
> "Mental Hygiene and Adjustment," *Review of Educational Research,* VI:5, December, 1936 (See especially Chapter VII.)
>
> Myers, C. Roger, *Toward Mental Health in School,* University of Toronto Press, Toronto, 1939
>
> Rivlin, H. N., *Educating for Adjustment,* D. Appleton-Century Company, Inc., New York, 1936
>
> Shaffer, L. F., *The Psychology of Adjustment,* Houghton Mifflin Company, Boston, 1936

Symonds, P. M., *Diagnosing Personality and Conduct,*
D. Appleton-Century Company, Inc., New York,
1931

Symonds, P. M., *The Mental Hygiene of the School
Child,* The Macmillan Company, New York, 1934
(See Chapters XIV to XVI.)

(*b*) *Physical Factors*

Is Your Child Ready for School? A Guide for Parents,
United States Office of Education, Health Education
Series, No. 13, Government Printing Office, Washing-
ton, D. C.

Phair, J. T., and others, *Health—A Handbook for
Teachers,* Ryerson Press, Toronto, 1938

Rogers, J. F., *What Every Teacher Should Know
About the Physical Condition of Her Pupils,* United
States Office of Education, Pamphlet No. 68, Gov-
ernment Printing Office, Washington, D. C., 1936

Terman, L. M., and Almack, J. C., *The Hygiene of the
School Child* (Revised), Houghton Mifflin Company,
Boston, 1929

(*c*) *Educational Factors*

Bronner, A. F., *The Psychology of Special Abilities
and Disabilities,* Little, Brown & Company, Boston,
1917

Brueckner, Leo J., *Diagnostic and Remedial Teaching
in Arithmetic,* The John C. Winston Company, Phila-
delphia, 1930

Educational Diagnosis, National Society for the Study
of Education, 34th Yearbook, Public School Publishing Company, Bloomington, Ill.

Monroe, Marion, *Children Who Cannot Read,* University of Chicago Press, Chicago, 1932

Monroe, Marion, and others, *Remedial Reading,*
Houghton Mifflin Company, Boston, 1937

Ruch, G. M., Knight, F. B., and Studebaker, J. W., *Mathematics and Life,* Scott, Foresman and Company, Chicago, 1937 (This contains simple but useful diagnostic tests for grades Seven and Eight.)

Schonell, F. J., *Diagnosis of Individual Differences in Arithmetic,* Oliver & Boyd, Ltd., Edinburgh, 1937

Stanger, M. A., and Donohue, E. K., *Prediction and Prevention of Reading Difficulties,* Oxford University Press, New York, 1937

Pamphlets, bulletins, and leaflets bearing on the physical and mental health of school children are available free of charge, or for a small charge, from many sources. Such publications as the following, for instance, can be obtained from the National Committee for Mental Hygiene, 50 West 50 Street, New York, N. Y.:

Behavior Problems of School Children

Mental Health in the Classroom (contains useful bibliography)

Understanding the Child—a quarterly magazine for teachers, containing accounts of recent developments of mental-hygiene significance coming from within the educational system.

Other sources of literature and information include:

United States Office of Education, Washington, D. C.

State or Provincial Department of Education

State or Provincial Department of Health

National Committee for Mental Hygiene, 50 West 50 Street, New York, N. Y.

National Committee for Mental Hygiene (Canada), 111 St. George Street, Toronto

Metropolitan Life Insurance Company, 1 Madison Avenue, New York, N. Y.

Canadian Welfare Council, Council House, Ottawa, Canada

Lists of publications can be secured by writing to the sources listed above.

APPENDIX

INTELLIGENCE TESTS

1. *Individual Tests.* The most commonly used individual intelligence test is the Terman revision of the *Binet-Simon Scale.* There have been two revisions of this scale, one published in 1916 and the other in 1937. Material and instructions for both may be obtained from Houghton Mifflin Company, Boston. The price list is as follows:

1916 Revision—Test Material	$ .80
Record Booklets (per set)	2.00
Manual (*The Measurement of Intelligence,* Terman)	2.00
1937 Revision—Test Material (alternative forms, L and M)	8.00 each
Record Booklets (alternative forms, L and M)	2.00 each set
Manual (*Measuring Intelligence,* Terman and Merrill)	2.25

2. *Group Tests*

Name	Grade	Time	Description and Publisher	Price
1. Pintner - Cunningham Primary Mental Tests	K-2	15	The test consists entirely of pictures—no reading. Age norms based on 30,000 cases. 16 pages. World Book Company, Yonkers	Per 25 with directions and scoring key—$1.25
2. Kuhlman - Anderson Tests (Fourth edition)	1-12	30	Separate test booklet for each grade level up to Grade 6. Educational Test Bureau, Inc., Minneapolis, Minn.	$1.25 per 25; manual, $.60

Name	Grade	Time	Description and Publisher	Price
3. Otis Group Intelligence Scale—Primary	K-4	40	Does not involve reading. 8 pages. World Book Company	$1.10 per 25, with directions and key
Advanced	K-12	60	Two equivalent forms. 11 pages. World Book Company	$1.10 per 25, with directions and key
4. Otis Self-Administering Tests of Mental Ability Intermediate	4-9	30	These tests can be given with few instructions. Scoring is rapid. 4 pages. World Book Company	$.80 per 25, with directions, key, and interpretation chart
Higher	9-college	30	As above	As above
5. National Intelligence Tests	3-8	30	Published in two forms, A and B. 12 pages. World Book Company	$1.25 per 25, with directions and key
6. Laycock Mental Ability Test	4-10	40	Standardized from Canadian data. One form. University of Saskatchewan Book Store, Saskatoon, Sask.	$1.00 per 25, with directions and scoring key
7. Dominion Group Test of Intelligence	8-9 (High-school entrance level)	50	Standardized from Canadian data. Department of Educational Research, University of Toronto, Bloor St. W., Toronto	Single copy, $.10; in quantity, $.03 each; directions and key, $.15

DIAGNOSTIC TESTS

The tests listed below are merely samples of hundreds of tests available in the educational field. They represent test techniques which are simple enough for the average teacher to administer.

Name	Grades	Description and Publisher	Price
1. Standardized Oral Reading Check Tests (W. S. Gray)	4 sets, covering grades 1-8	A simple reading test which serves to measure progress as well as to secure detailed information about the specific nature of difficulties (Public School Publishing Company, Bloomington, Illinois)	$1.50 per packet 100 tests (20 of each of the 5 tests). Sample set, with directions, 50c
2. Gates Silent Reading Tests (A. I. Gates)	3-8 (also primary series)	A more complicated test procedure than the above. Four types of tests cover different aspects of pur-	One form of each type: $2.10 per 100 copies

Name	Grades	Description and Publisher	Price
		poseful reading; three equivalent forms in each type test. (Bureau of Publications, Teachers College, Columbia University, New York, N. Y.)	
3. Gates - Russell Spelling Diagnosis Tests (A. I. Gates and D. H. Russell)	2-6	Test designed to reveal the extent and nature of errors in spelling (Bureau of Publications, Teachers College, Columbia University, New York, N. Y.)	5c per test; 60c per manual. Sample set, 60c
4. Compass Diagnostic Tests in Arithmetic (Ruch, Knight, Greene, and Studebaker) .	2-8	Some twenty sections covering every arithmetic process by grades (Scott, Foresman and Company, Chicago, Ill.)	Various prices, depending on sections; specimen set with manual, 60c

NOTE. For a comprehensive and critical review of all the latest educational and other tests, see *Nineteen Thirty-eight Mental Measurements Yearbook,* edited by Oscar Buros, Rutgers University Press, New Brunswick, N. J.

GUIDE FOR SECURING DATA FOR DIAGNOSIS

Date...............

Name.............. Date of Birth...... Address.......

School .... Room... Grade... Time in Grade...

Problem (State in very few words exactly what the problem is, its duration, and how it developed. Give only facts, not opinions. If the report is being given at the request of a clinic or a social agency, indicate the fact here.)

Information from School Records

Age on entering school (years and months)........ Grades repeated ....

Attendance (If irregular state the cause—truancy? ill-health?) ....

Other schools attended (How long in each?)................

Physical examinations (Give the date, report, and recommendations of the school medical officer. If no report is available, give your own estimate of the child's physique and any special difficulties, eyesight, hearing, lameness, poor posture, etc.)

Psychological examination (If the child has been examined by the psychologist, give the date, nature of the test, result, and recommendations made. If any group tests have been administered, indicate the date they were given, their nature, and the result.)

Present Status at School

Standing and progress (Indicate the subjects in which he is failing at present. What is the approximate grade level of his achievement in these? Is he showing better than average ability in any subject?)

General appearance (Describe the physical appearance of the child, his tendencies to neatness and cleanliness, and his general activity tendencies. Is he overactive or underactive? Has he good self-control, or is he impulsive? any nervous habits, such as muscle twitching or nail biting? Describe his speech. Are there any defects? Is he talkative? Is he learning bad speech habits from home?)

Intellectual development (Under this heading include your own estimate of the child's intelligence, his habits and methods of work, his ability to pay attention and concentrate on one thing at a time. Has he good manual dexterity? Has the child displayed particular interest in intellectual, artistic, or practical pursuits?)

Social development (Of what character are his friends? Are they younger or older? Is he sociable or does he tend to be a withdrawing and solitary type? Is he shy in school, or forward? matter-of-fact or daydreaming? How does he play? Does he always want to be boss or does he usually allow himself to be led and influenced by others? Is he polite and obedient? honest and truthful? kind and generous? Has he any particular social interests—clubs, societies, and so on?)

Emotional development (Has he normal emotional stability or does he cry on the slightest provocation? Has he any obvious fears or worries? What is his characteristic mood— cheerful or gloomy? good-natured or irritable? Is he unduly sensitive or easily discouraged and depressed? Has he feelings of inferiority? Is he unduly aggressive? bullying? jealous? Does he hold grudges? resent authority?)

Other comments (Record here any other special characteristics or peculiarity traits you have noticed in the child; also any special difficulties.)

NOTE. In reporting on children for clinics or agencies the above outline with the information suggested is sufficient.

Information from the Parents

Position in family (Indicate how many brothers and sisters he has and how many are older and how many younger. Thus F2, M5, X, M10, F11 would be a simple way of indicating that the child had a younger sister of 2, a younger brother of 5, an older brother of 10, and an older sister of 11.)

Parents (State your impression of the parents, noting such factors as poor health and unfavorable personality traits: irritable? unsympathetic? ignorant? What is their attitude to the child and his problems? economic status? social interests?)

Home (Is there satisfactory accommodation for the child for sleeping, recreation, and so on? Is the home crowded? Are the children neglected? Is the atmosphere depressing?)

Developmental history (Without great detail record any striking retardation in time of teething, walking, and talking; any serious illness; accidents; operations; difficulty in establishing good habits of eating, sleeping, and elimination.)

Special circumstances (Record any circumstances in the home not covered above which may be contributing to the child's difficulty—harsh inconsistent discipline; more favored brother or sister; bad examples and loose social and moral standards set by other members of the family.)

Information from the Child

Personal interview (Give an account of the significant points coming out in conversation with the child—attitude to home; to school; to yourself; to the problem for which he is being studied; special interests and wishes.)

Special diagnostic procedures (Record the nature and results of intelligence and educational tests administered.)

General Summary and Interpretation

(Give an account here in two or three sentences of what you think are the pertinent factors in the case.)

Proposed Remedial Procedure

(Outline briefly the various suggestions you would like to see carried out. Particularly important, of course, are the procedures that can be arranged for in the school.)

CHAPTER V

LIMITED MENTAL ABILITY

I. INDIVIDUAL DIFFERENCES IN INTELLIGENCE

It will be recalled from the brief discussion of differences that occur in the development of children [1] that no two children are alike. In discussing "child development" we may speak of averages; it is permissible, even, to think of the general characteristics of children of a certain age, say eight years old. Yet when we are considering an individual child we must realize that at any given age there is a great range of physical and mental characteristics possible. Intelligence is a case in point. If the intelligence quotients of a thousand ten-year-old children were estimated according to some standard scale, there would be a wide variation in the results. If these quotients were distributed graphically according to their frequency, the typical bell-shaped curve of normal probability would result. [2] About 60% of the children would have I.Q.'s between 90 and 110, and, although they would represent rather wide differences within that spread, they are usually lumped together and designated as of "average" or "normal" intelligence—normal being, by definition, that which characterizes the majority. On one side of this average group are the 20% who are below average in intelligence; and on the other side, the 20% who are above the average. The general problem to be discussed in this chapter is that of educating the group of children whose intelligence is below the average.

[1] See page 8.
[2] See page 99.

This group can be further subdivided according to more or less arbitrary standards. On the basis of intelligence quotients alone, for example, such children can be classified as "dull normals" (I.Q. of 80-90), "borderline defectives" (I.Q. of 70-80), and those who are definitely "feeble-minded" (I.Q. below 70).

If the child is dull and slow to learn, he presents certain problems in formal education the procedures of which are adapted to the education of normal children. If he is too low in ability to work well in a regular class, he may be managed in a special class set aside for exceptional children of this sort. If his deficiency is so great that even this arrangement will not be of any value to him, he may have to be cared for by the parents at home or by a special training school for mental defectives. This chapter deals with ways of adapting the school curriculums, organization, and teaching methods (which were originally intended for children of average ability) to meet the needs of these less gifted children.

Education has long recognized the necessity of meeting these needs. Indeed, such special techniques as intelligence tests were first devised to help the teacher diagnose the cause of classroom difficulties represented by children below average in general ability. By the use of these special techniques, teachers developed increasing insight into the meaning of limited mental ability, and organized special curricular and extracurricular programs to help solve the problems that the diagnosis had clarified. Teachers became interested in the individual children who presented these problems, and took pride in following the children through school and, after school, into their occupational and vocational life. In this way, children of low intelligence were responsible for bringing to the attention of many teachers the importance of educational end products. It has been said that the special course of study offered these children in some communities is superior in every way to the "regular" program. Without subscribing to this statement, the authors believe that there is much of value for all teachers in these special programs.

II. SOME COMMON MISCONCEPTIONS

There is a popular conception that many dull children "wake up" later and become normal or even clever. The evidence on the whole is against this belief. Sudden gains, which may appear in certain cases, are on closer investigation usually found to be due not to a sudden growth of intelligence but to a new-found interest or better motivation or improved physical health or the removal of emotional difficulties.

Reference has already been made to the work of Wellman [3] in connection with the influence of environment on intellectual development. In 1926 Freeman [4] reported a similar effect in the case of children removed from orphanages and placed in good foster homes. In these children the I.Q. rose, after a few years, by an average of 7.5 points. These results should be received with caution. Many of the test items in the Binet Intelligence Test place a premium on a knowledge of language and social customs. It is conceivable that the children from drab, impoverished, environmental situations would show less ability on such tests than children from better homes, where the environment is rich in possibilities for language

[3] See page 15.
[4] Freeman, F. N., *Mental Tests,* Houghton Mifflin Company, Boston, 1926.

development and social experience. The rise in I.Q. may be caused, therefore, by the increased skill that the child develops in using his intelligence to advantage and in ways which give him higher scores on the relatively crude tests of the measuring instrument.

Teachers should thus not place too great reliance on the hope that the dull child, in a better environment, will show significant change in capacity. His behavior, his knowledge, and his general intellectual habits may greatly improve; yet if the intelligence of a child has been carefully assessed by a competent psychologist or psychiatrist, there is little hope that it will be altered materially by any change in environment or training. It is important, therefore, that in any environment we direct the child's intellectual capacity wisely and develop fully his inborn potentialities.

There is also a popular conception that the dull children continue their mental growth longer than the bright children, and thus catch up eventually. While there does seem to be some variation in the ages at which the mental growth curve ceases to rise, the variation has no correlation with intelligence. The available scientific evidence all points to the fact that children who are definitely and inherently dull and slow in intellectual development tend to remain relatively dull as adults, at least in terms of their scores on intelligence tests. This does not mean that a healthy adjustment to life cannot be made by dull children. They may have assets of temperament and personality that more than compensate for a deficiency in intelligence. The fact remains, however, that it is dangerous and misleading to teach parents to expect that their dull child will in time "catch up with the others."

It must be remembered, of course, that what has been said above refers only to available scientific evidence. Future research into medical and educational needs may extend considerably the degree to which initial dullness in children may be overcome. At all times, however, practical policies must necessarily be governed by the existing state of our knowledge.

III. THE SLOW-LEARNING CHILD AT SCHOOL

In discussing classroom programs for the slow-learning child, let us first consider those children whose mental ability is below average but who are able to make a good adjustment in the regular classroom, provided the teacher is willing to give some special attention to them. It is impossible to define this group in terms of I.Q. alone, because it includes children whose ability to adjust depends on so many other factors. Cultural, social, and economic background, previously acquired skills and interests, and emotional stability are a few such factors which may determine the effect of regular classroom work on these children. We have seen children with I.Q.'s as low as 70 thoroughly happy with younger and brighter children in an ordinary grade classroom. On the other hand, the reverse is also true. Children who have ability close to the average occasionally do not seem to fit in happily with their classmates, and often it is necessary to give these children some special educational supervision in an auxiliary class for a while, until they are able once more to meet the challenge of their grade. In all this, however, flexibility of the grading program should be maintained.

A teacher's problems with dull children frequently arise soon after the children enter school. Authorities agree that, under usual conditions, a mental age of at least six years is necessary in order to learn to read.[5] Some place the basic reading age at six years and six months. The dull child, on entering the first grade at six years of age, may have a mental age of less than five years. Therefore, under normal conditions, he would be expected to have difficulty in learning to read and in keeping up with the average child of his grade in other divisions of the work. Ordinarily, he comes to school willingly, with the sense of adventure which this new experience should create; but inasmuch as he is unable to compete with his "average" and, therefore, brighter comrades, his attitude of expectancy is changed to a feeling of failure and inadequacy. Few of us like the tasks at which we fail; and this child's first experience of school and schoolwork is an experience of failure. The result is indifference towards school, or even distaste for school activities—an attitude which later progress may have difficulty in changing.

After the child has met failure a sufficient number of times, the teacher of the first grade may adopt one of two alternative procedures. He may try to increase the child's learning rate by "motivating" him to work harder, to do homework, and by giving him extra drill. This pressure may bring about the desired result in certain children, but more frequently it causes an intensification of the feeling of inadequacy and failure, with manifestation of emotional maladjustment or nervousness, as described in an earlier chapter. As the second alternative, the teacher may allow the child to busy himself with whatever seems to interest him, allowing his activity to go more or less undirected so long as the child remains quiet. The teacher does not usually allow such a child to

[5] But see, for instance, Gates, A. I., "The Necessary Mental Age for Beginning Reading," *Elementary School Journal*, 37:497-508, March, 1937.

go his own way in this manner unless he has already decided that the child will repeat the grade in the next year. The teacher may rationalize his position by arguing that if the child repeats the grade the following year, his intelligence and mental age will have increased to such a degree that he will be able to make progress at the expected rate. Meanwhile, however, damage will have been done. It is so difficult to develop and maintain healthy attitudes toward work, and toward life as a whole, if the thrill and satisfaction of successful achievement is denied.

The story, begun in this unfortunate way, repeats itself with monotonous regularity throughout the elementary school. The progress of the child with limited ability through the grades is frequently retarded. If promotions are made only in June, no opportunity is given him to make progress from one grade to another in the middle of the term. This usually means that he must spend all of one or two years extra in each grade. When he is promoted, his "standing" is usually low. In the traditional educational system he has little chance of securing good "standing" in any of the academic subjects. He is pushed, coaxed, and hurried by the teacher, whose reputation or even continued employment may depend upon getting a high percentage of his pupils "through" the examinations. The child is criticized, cajoled, and scolded by his parents, who are dissatisfied with his report card and often make him the subject of invidious comparison with other children. Occasionally, too, his classmates may taunt and tease him for his deficiency.

He may finally manage to pass Grade Eight at the age of fifteen to seventeen. If he is allowed to go to an academic high school his difficulties become even more marked. The abstract thought involved in the study of mathematics, literature, history, and science is beyond his capacity or comprehension and is quite unsuited to his needs. The brighter children of the dull group benefit greatly from a secondary education directed along more practical lines. However, few communities, apart from the larger cities, offer technical or vocational courses as alternatives to academic high school. Often, even when suitable facilities are available, parents have a pathetic belief in the efficacy of the formal high-school course. They insist that their children make an attempt at it irrespective of their interests or abilities. To these parents, matriculation has been persistently upheld as the only gateway to business opportunities. Sometimes, in forcing a high-school education upon their children, they are really compensating for the long-since-thwarted ambitions for an education for themselves.

The results of this traditional educational policy are not far to seek. The discouraging effect of continued failure, and the inhibitions resulting from being continually forced to perform tasks which are just a little too difficult, are manifest in the high incidence of problems among such children. In an effort to adjust to a difficult situation, these children commonly develop antisocial tendencies and other symptoms of emotional and nervous tension. Hence, among delinquents, one finds an unexpected number of children with low I.Q.'s.[6]

A study by one of the present writers [7] showed that one of the most important causes of emotional and personality difficulties in children was the feeling of inferiority

[6] Burt, C. L., *The Young Delinquent* (Third Revised Edition), University of London Press, Ltd., London, 1938.

[7] Laycock, S. R., "Adjustments of Inferior and Superior School Children," *Journal of Social Psychology*, 1933:4; 355-366.

brought about by school failure. Many of the problems were due to the efforts made by these children to compensate for this feeling of inferiority. Profanity and smoking, for example, could be interpreted as attempts to bolster up threatened self-esteem. The chief motive seemed to be the urge to prove to everyone, including themselves, that they were really "he-men." The same motive was found in many cases of stealing, where the proceeds of the thefts were used to buy treats for friends; and also in such behavior as bullying, fighting, and boasting, where the compensation for feelings of inadequacy was more obvious. Some children reacted to failure by developing extreme sensitiveness, shyness, and timidity.

Many of these difficulties were clearly shown by a boy of nearly twelve. He was in Grade Three. His teacher complained that he was extremely lazy, had difficulty in paying attention to his work, was talkative, overactive, and excitable. In addition, he was frequently untruthful and evasive. He could never be trusted. He had the reputation of being the ringleader of a small gang, and was one of a group of boys discovered shoplifting in a downtown store. He was described as being the worst boy in the class; and the principal was seriously considering expelling him. His school record showed that he had started school at the age of six, had repeated Grade One and Grade Two. The teacher described his home as inferior. The mother was a sensitive little woman who did not seem to know how to handle the boy at home. The school medical officer had reported that he was in normal health, although small for his age.

In appearance the boy was very untidy, dressed in rather ragged dirty clothes. His mental age was nine years and nine months, and his I.Q. was 82. A previous test by means of the Dominion Group Test of Intelligence had estimated his I.Q. to be 85. He co-operated with the psychologist willingly, but tended to give up very easily. His most important asset was his genial and friendly cheerfulness. His mood changed rapidly, however, whenever he was faced with a problem; and when the psychologist attempted to discuss his difficulties, he became defensive, curt, and sullen. He claimed to be only ten years old, instead of nearly twelve. (This is a common reaction of dull children who feel the unfortunate effects of their failure.) He was a persuasive talker when allowed to discuss things which interested him; and he exhibited a keen imagination. He described vividly how people were conspiring against him to get him into trouble. He was anxious to recount personal experiences to prove persecution. His vocabulary, while picturesque, was limited. Treatment was rather difficult, as it should have been begun years earlier. An effort was made, however, to give the child emotional and social security in school and in his contacts outside school. A new classroom procedure was prescribed for him, and he was encouraged to join the Scouts and a boys' club at the church, where he could develop a sense of achievement and personal worth through games and sports.

This is a typical clinical picture of a child with limited mental ability who has not received adequate educational guidance and stimulation.

The way in which the teacher deals with the problem of dullness depends on the nature of the limitations of the children. Popular designations such as "low I.Q." or "slow learning ability" are not helpful here. For use in planning an educational program, a more detailed analysis is necessary, and to this end an attempt is made in the following few paragraphs to outline the chief characteristics of dull children.

1. Usually they do not have a good mastery of previous learning. They travel slowly and need frequent and carefully planned reviews—reviews that are not "drill"

but rather frequent opportunities to use their recently acquired skills in problem situations.

2. Their span of interest and attention is short; and, as a result, they need short units of work. This does not mean that the subject periods must be shortened. These children, however, must not be expected to pay attention for long periods just for the purpose of paying attention. There should be frequent introduction of new focuses of interest.

3. The fundamental difficulty underlying the apparent short span of attention may be the fact that dull children cannot keep many ideas in mind. A mentally retarded child may work happily for long periods at a simple job well within the limits of his ability. In a rural school recently a child with an I.Q. of 72 worked busily and happily all morning sawing up short blocks of wood for a classroom project. Activity which would quickly bore the average child was interesting to him and provided adequate educational challenge.

The teacher's problem is to elevate the complexity and usefulness of such work to the highest level concomitant with successful achievement. Remembering how difficult it is for dull children to retain ideas, the teacher will make a special effort, whenever possible, to see that new phases of a subject are presented *one at a time*. What is new will then stand out vividly against a background of familiar and well-assimilated material, and will more easily be brought into relation to the subject as a whole. For example, the boy who was sawing off blocks of wood might be easily encouraged to measure the marks for the saw cuts. From this point, simple calculation by the child for determining the number of blocks available in one piece of timber could be made.

4. Children of limited mental ability do not comprehend quickly the full significance of ideas and relationships, and, as a result, questions must be clear and specific, and assertions must be clear-cut and definite.

5. Dull children cannot make the same associations or analogies as can ordinary children. Nearly all new teachers make the mistake of omitting steps and failing to bring out the relationship involved in a unit of work. New teachers, in the words of a veteran, "seem to have no idea how stupid people are." Certainly every experienced teacher will recognize something of truth in the motto, "The longer you teach, the less you assume." A good teacher will assume very little when he is dealing with children below the average in intelligence. Every step in the solution of a problem must be brought out vividly, so that it is clear beyond a shadow of a doubt.

6. The dull child cannot organize ideas or facts as well as those of "average" intelligence. Organizing material is essentially a matter of seeing the relations existing between its various parts; and "relational thinking" is one of the fundamental attributes of intelligence. Situations and material, therefore, must be fairly well organized for dull children, or else be of such a nature as to require very little organization. Sometimes even children with good minds get into habits of poorly integrated, slipshod thinking. If this is possible in bright children, it must be guarded against even more carefully in the dull. If the material itself is not beyond the level of the pupil, good habits of organizing it can be encouraged and developed by the patient teacher.

7. The dull do not transfer ability from one situation to another as effectively as do average children. As a result, more effort must be made to provide *specifically* for

transfer, and more type situations approximating those which the child will actually encounter in life must be used. Recent experimental studies indicate that automatic transfer occurs only to a very small extent, and that the lower one goes in the scale of intelligence the less the transfer. In fact, those who work with the very dull always comment on the absence of transfer, even to a problem practically identical with one that is long since familiar and understood. This means that health habits, mental-hygiene habits, and desirable reactions of a social, emotional, and intellectual nature must be specifically developed in the dull child; and that subjects proposed for their curriculum should be such as will have a practical value in their daily lives.

Since the problem of the child with defective or limited mental ability arises during the first years of school, our attention must be directed to the primary grades if we are to deal with it effectively. Many modern schools have no grade promotions before Grade Three. During this period, training in "group living" is stressed, as are health and other aspects of citizenship. In order to facilitate the teaching of the "three R's" children may be grouped together in various ways; but tests, grade promotions, and highly competitive learning are not features of the system. Those who come to school with a mental age below six are given kindergarten work until they are ready for reading. In this way, the teaching is individualized to a high degree, with no sacrifice of the benefit of group experience. Above all, the disastrous results of immediate failure are postponed; and the child has an opportunity to establish a healthy attitude toward work and school.

If the teacher finds himself in a school where some such system is not in use, he can still do much to safeguard the personalities of inferior children. A realization of the child's mental age and slow development will help him to modify the work so that the child does achieve results and obtains that sense of personal worth which is so important for the healthy personality. The child may find these personal satisfactions in handicraft, in errands or school duties that create a sense of responsibility, and in extraclassroom activities. The teacher should avoid involving the child in unfair and unequal competition. When the child cannot keep pace with his companions, the teacher should never resort to high-pressure methods, scorn, and ridicule. In other words, the child should acquire standards that are commensurate with his ability.

Above the primary grades it is more difficult to deal with such handicapped children in the traditional organization. Gradually, social and emotional values, together with sound all-round development, are becoming goals in education as acceptable as mere academic achievement. Granted this, it becomes not only possible but necessary to modify the curriculum and standards for dull normals so that they can attain success with reasonable effort. Some school systems form special classes (or even schools) for dull children, where the more abstract parts of the academic courses are eliminated, and practical courses in handwork and, later, shopwork and household science are substituted. Whatever the curriculum, traditional or otherwise, there should be sufficient flexibility to enable the intelligent teacher to adapt the work to the needs of every child. Even in rural schools, the teacher can alleviate the difficulties of dull children by concentrating on minimum requirements, and by taking care to see that the pupil experiences success in *some* aspects of his academic work and in the practical courses.

Extraclassroom activities, athletics, and classroom responsibilities should be liberally utilized and should not be the special reward of the gifted and superior children. Many schools have devised a system where the brighter students are freed from some of the grind of academic work for such activities as art, dramatics, shopwork, household science, and various cultural and broadening exercises. In the meantime, the dull normals, who, of all children, need practical and expressive activities, are forced to spend all their time on academic subjects and drill. They suffer in a threefold way. They have to spend all day on work that is more difficult for them than for their brighter and more fortunate schoolmates. In addition they carry a stigma because of their failure to be released from the academic grind. Finally, they miss the very part of education that they would find most enjoyable and helpful.

It is important to differentiate the child of normal ability who will not work from the child with subnormal ability who has stopped trying because he is tired of continual failure. The child who is keeping step educationally with his intellectual growth in terms of mental age cannot, logically, be considered backward or retarded at school. He may be retarded compared with the average child, but compared with himself (the only legitimate standard to use) he is making satisfactory progress. His educational quotient [8] is one hundred or more.

---

[8] The Educational Quotient (E.Q.) or Achievement Ratio is equal to the Educational Age (EA), in terms of the age level of progress made in school, divided by the Mental Age (MA) of the child, expressed as a percentage. Thus, $E.Q. = \frac{EA}{MA} \times 100$. Real educational retardation, therefore, exists only when this quotient is much under a hundred. Children with an E.Q. much over a hundred must be classed with those who are doing exceptionally well at school.

At the risk of needless repetition, once again it is urged that respect for, and interest in, the pupil as a personality striving toward certain goals, perhaps but dimly defined, must eventually lead to some individualization of treatment. Sarcasm, ridicule, and punishment have little place in the education of these children; and excess drill, driving, and high-pressure tactics are not necessary. We should not force them to meet defined standards, but rather help them achieve satisfactory objectives.

IV. SPECIAL CLASSES FOR CHILDREN WITH LIMITED MENTAL ABILITY

There are always a few dull children who, despite the efforts of the teacher, are unhappy in the regular grades. Frequently their mental ability and intelligence is too limited to enable them to learn, even though the total situation is considerably reduced in complexity. Sometimes the chief difficulty is a temperamental one and can be corrected if the child is given an opportunity to regain stability and confidence in an ungraded class for a few months.

Where special classes are provided in the school system, various definitions of their population have been devised. Some municipalities have regulations stating arbitrarily that such classes are for children with an I.Q. under 75; some accept children for these classes who have I.Q.'s within the range 50-80. These classes are usually called *auxiliary, opportunity,* or *ungraded* classes. Some cities have organized whole schools for children with I.Q.'s between 70-90. In these schools there is a modified academic program with special vocational and handicraft opportunities. These special schools are usually known as nonacademic, handicraft, or junior vocational schools. Often they are limited to one sex.

In rural schools the organization of special classes may be impossible. However, much can be done towards modifying the curriculum and even towards introducing some handwork and crafts. If the teacher adopts the spirit of the new courses of study which are being developed in many communities in the United States and Canada, he will have little difficulty in arranging the details. We should remember that education should aim to develop health habits, good character traits, good social and emotional reactions, and, within the limits of ability, good thinking and intellectual habits. Arithmetic, for example, must be taught in a manner to be of actual material value in the pupils' lives. For dull children this means, at the most, the ability to make change and simple purchases. Reading, also, must have a close relation to the children's needs. The ability to read street and store signs, the names of products and commodities, price signs, advertisements, newspapers, and simple stories for pleasure constitutes the basic need. Nearly half the classroom work should be handwork.[9]

From the foregoing outline it will be obvious that the emphasis in work with dull children is not placed on tests, examinations, or promotions. The limited intellectual capacity of the children and the kind of occupations for which they are fitted make it unwise to attempt to put them through the usual grade examinations unless there are exceptional circumstances. This is particularly true of the "high-school entrance" examinations.

[9] The teacher is referred to the books listed at the end of this chapter for help and practical suggestions concerning special methods useful in working with these children.

The general organization of special classes for backward children will not be discussed here, since, in every case, it should be carried out under the direction of an inspector, a supervisor, or a government official. The selection of suitable candidates should be made by an expert on the basis of surveys that include mental tests and information from the school records, the school nurse, the home, the teacher, and the principal.

Many teachers, however, work in districts where it is not possible, at present, for the child to attend a special class. What can be done in such a case?

(1) The local supervisor should be consulted and the data laid before him. If, after investigation, he agrees that the child needs some special adaptation of curriculum and teaching technique, then the teacher may plan carefully how this can best be arranged.

(2) With the supervisor's guidance, the teacher should modify the curriculum so that the academic aspects are suited to the child's needs.

(3) He may introduce handwork, drawing, and similar exercises in a way that will not embarrass the child by calling attention to his difficulties. The teacher should see that the child gets such opportunity in classroom projects and extra-classroom activities as he can use to advantage.

(4) The method of dealing with the child must increase the child's sense of personal worth. Otherwise it is ineffective. If the child is in any sense stigmatized by the special procedures, his personality will be injured, and the teacher is not succeeding in his efforts.

(5) The teacher should remember that most dull children can, if their personality is safeguarded, become useful, self-respecting, and self-supporting citizens. He may remember, also, that it takes a competent, intelligent, understanding, and resourceful teacher to teach a very dull child either in a special

class or in an ordinary grade. Teachers may regard this fact as a challenge to their professional skill and to their understanding of individual differences in social contribution.

V. CHILDREN WHO SHOULD BE EXCLUDED

Occasionally we encounter in schools children who should never have been allowed to attend. Their intellectual ability is so low that they belong among the "imbeciles" or "idiots" and are really unable to manage either themselves or their affairs. They are usually recognizable by their retarded development, lack of ability to learn, and by various physical stigmata. By *stigmata* are meant defects such as a misshapen head, peculiarly shaped ears, a cleft palate, or distorted facial features with a gaping (and often drooling) mouth.

If children of this intellectual level come to school at all, they usually do so at seven or eight years of age. Even at that time their mental age will be under four years. They differ so greatly from the average that they have no place in the ordinary classroom, and are usually excluded by the school doctor. The usual practice is to educate them in special institutions organized as training schools for mental defectives. Almost every province and state now has at least one of these institutions. When children are certified by a physician as being suitable for such a school, they are admitted for a short or a long period, depending on the circumstances. Some children, of course, must live in an institution all their lives for the protection of themselves and others.

In some communities the higher-grade imbeciles are taught in "occupational centers" to which they are brought daily by busses or guides. This method is used to some extent in Great Britain. Education in such centers is devoted mainly to the establishment of simple habits of health, cleanliness, play, and construction.

No matter what technique is used for the supervision and training of very defective children, it is well for the teacher to remember that the problem is still an *educational* one. Even if the mentally defective child has to be taught how to achieve bowel and bladder control, how to talk, how to walk, how to lace shoes, how to discriminate forms, colors, tastes, and sounds, he is still undergoing a learning process. Idiots and imbeciles, like other children, need medical attention for illness and for the removal or treatment of physical defects. Beyond that, they need training that is essentially the task of education. They, too, in accord with our present democratic conception of equality of opportunity, must have the chance to develop the most wholesome personality that their limited mental capacity allows.

VI. EDUCATING THE PARENTS

One of the most difficult of all the tasks a teacher has to perform is that of explaining to a father and mother that their child is definitely retarded and may need special educational provision. It is fortunate if the child is diagnosed as dull before his handicap leads him into trouble. Once the parent is called to the school because the child has been misbehaving, the chances are against the easy establishment of a favorable relationship. This is especially so if the teacher or principal states firmly and unequivocally that the child is "mental" and should be placed in a special class for "mental children."

It is far better to select the retarded child (who will likely require special attention) and interview his parents early. A beginning may be found in an emphasis on all the child's good points that, by any stretch of the imagination, can be thought of. Then gradually the subject of different children developing at different rates may be broached. The parents may be told that some children remain like little children much longer than others, and learn more slowly. Then the suggestion may be made to the parents that their child is one of these, followed by an explanation that modern education has at last taken notice of such children and has provided special facilities for them. It is important to say that the teacher must spend much more time with each child individually, and that the child is therefore to derive more benefit from attendance at school. When the teacher is tactfully frank in this way, there is usually very little trouble in gaining the parents' full co-operation. It goes without saying that special classes for retarded children should be looked upon as "opportunity classes," a point of view that should be emphasized in all conversation with parents or home and school groups. The use of such a phrase avoids the possibility of the arousal of unfortunate attitudes toward the project.

VII. SPECIAL EDUCATION AS AN ASPECT OF GENERAL EDUCATION

Many people think that special education is an extra frill in modern education, added through sentiment. It is here pointed out that education for all children, whether average, gifted, retarded, or physically handicapped, should be dominated by *one aim*—the desire to promote the sound, many-sided development of the child. School organization, curriculums, and teaching methods are only *means* to this end. They must give the child opportunities to develop according to his ability and his needs. They must be fitted to the child. Special curriculums, classes, and institutions are provided for the purpose of giving to children who deviate from the average the same chance of wholesome development as is given to normal children. Special education is, therefore, general education applied to special problems.

REFERENCES

For further guidance in the problem of the slow-learning child, the teacher is referred to the following:

Amoss, H. E., and DeLaporte, L. H., *Training Handicapped Children*, Ryerson Press, Toronto, 1933

Bentley, J. E., *Problem Children*, W. W. Norton & Company, New York; George J. McLeod, Ltd., Toronto, 1936

Burt, Cyril, *The Backward Child*, D. Appleton-Century Company, Inc., New York, 1937

Group Activities for Mentally Retarded Children—A Symposium, United States Office of Education, Bulletin No. 7, Government Printing Office, Washington, D. C., 1933.

Guide to Curriculum Adjustment for Mentally Retarded Children, United States Office of Education, Bulletin No. 11, Government Printing Office, Washington, D. C., 1936

Ingram, C. P., *The Education of the Slow-learning Child*, World Book Company, Yonkers-on-Hudson, 1935

Mort, P. R., *The Individual Pupil*, American Book Company, New York, 1928

Schools and Classes for Feeble-minded and Subnormal Children, United States Office of Education, Bulletin No. 5, Government Printing Office, Washington, D. C., 1928

Teachers' Problems with Exceptional Children, III (Mentally Retarded Children), United States Office of Education, Pamphlet No. 49, Government Printing Office, Washington, D. C., 1934

There are several good periodicals dealing with the education of the retarded child:

(a) *Special Class Teacher*—published three times a year by the Auxiliary Class Teachers' Section of the Ontario Educational Association, 361 Jarvis Street, Toronto, Ontario

(b) *Journal of Exceptional Children*—published monthly October to May, by Harley Z. Wooden, East Lansing, Michigan

CHAPTER VI

SUPERIOR MENTAL ABILITY

I. BRIGHT CHILDREN AT SCHOOL

In any "unselected" and sufficiently large group of children (to repeat once more the now familiar facts concerning the distribution of intelligence), 60% are found to be of "average" mental capacity; 20%, below average; and the remaining 20%, above. In this chapter we are concerned with the 20% having ability above average, children whose I.Q.'s are over 110 and who are commonly designated "superior or gifted." As before, this superior group can be subdivided into groups according to I.Q. These subgroups are "superior intelligence," "very superior intelligence," and "genius or near-genius," relating respectively to children with I.Q.'s of 110-120, 120-140, and over 140. It is extremely doubtful, however, if such refinement or such grouping is of advantage in education, because there are other aspects of personality which are often of more importance than native intelligence. The disposition and temperament of a child may be such that, having only average intellectual capacity, he is nevertheless definitely a "superior" child. The reverse, of course, is also true. A child may have excellent mental ability and still not be able to use it efficiently and effectively because of personality shortcomings.

Children with above-average intelligence, entering school at six years of age, tend to find the work of Grade One easy, because their mental ages are from six to eighteen months in advance of that of the average child. As habits of work and attitudes toward school are likely to be formed in the early years, it is important that these children be given an opportunity to apply themselves to tasks at which they can succeed only after an expenditure of effort. Their interest in school activities should be captured at the outset and held by work that is a reasonable challenge to them.

The following illustration from an educational clinic represents the behavior of a "gifted" child. The boy was eight years and ten months old. He had a mental age of eleven years and four months, and an I.Q. of 128. He was in Grade Four in an excellent school. His father was a moderately successful lawyer; his mother used to be a music teacher; and his home background, generally, was good. He had begun school when he was a little over six years of age and had already been advanced one grade ahead of his age group. He was very well developed physically, above average in height and weight for his age. His teacher reported him as being a "superior child" in every way. She said that the boy's only difficulty was a slight tendency toward slapdash habits of work. He always handed in his work before the others, and did not trouble to read it over before doing so. He seemed to be satisfied with less than his best possible level of achievement. He mixed well with his classmates and had no particular personality maladjustment, unless his tendency to talk about himself and his home a little too much could be considered as such.

When he was examined, he appeared to enjoy the process of the psychological examination very much. He had a very free, offhand manner, and remarked spontaneously that some of the intelligence tests were very easy for him. He said that he had read all Aesop's fables, and showed some enthusiasm about astronomy. Apparently he had telephoned, of his own accord, to the professor of astronomy at the university to ask if he might visit the observatory to look through the telescope. He spoke in a clear, deliberate manner, and chose his words with care. In the Stanford-Binet Intelligence Test he was successful in all the items at the ten-year level. His vocabulary, ability to interpret pictures and fables, and his ability to remember figures were equivalent to the twelve-year level, and he passed one test at the fourteen-year level.

II. THE CHARACTERISTICS OF SUPERIOR CHILDREN

There are many interesting psychological differences between superior children and average children as a group. Some of these are as follows:

(1) Superior children grasp more easily the essentials of a topic under discussion; and, while they need review, they need much less of it than that required by average children working with the traditional curriculums. Sometimes this characteristic presents a problem, since many gifted children do not wish to be bothered with the monotonous task of learning spelling, mastering number combinations, and retaining factual material. The teacher must help these children to realize that facts are the raw materials of thinking. They should learn that the achievement of any great invention, work of art, military campaign, and so forth, has invariably necessitated a willingness to toil indefatigably over areas of tedious detail. Strictly speaking, genius may be more than just "an infinite capacity for taking pains," yet without that capacity the most brilliant genius may fail to justify itself in any tangible way. Children should have the opportunity of appreciating that special ability and talent involves special social responsibility.

(2) The interest span of these children is longer than that of average children, since they are more able to re-

late the topic under discussion to other aspects of the whole project. They are thus able to do work that requires sustained interest, whether in formal classroom procedures or in projects that involve plans for activity over a considerable period of time. It is as if superior ability has a noticeably superior momentum.

(3) Superior children are able to retain more details in mind, and therefore in the learning situation they do not require the ideational simplicity prescribed for dull children. In the ordinary class, schoolwork as presented to "dull normal" and "average" children may be too simple for superior children. It may bore them and represent an insufficient challenge to them. In general terms, it may be said that the complexity of the learning situation should always be suited to the child's ability, neither above nor below it.

(4) Superior children see the significance of ideas quickly. A pedantic teacher, who elaborates details needlessly, is likely to bore and annoy them and to kill their interest. To give facts, data, or explanations which the children themselves could have contributed is possibly an indication of poor teaching.

(5) The organization of useful knowledge involves classifying ideas, seeing the relation of each to the other and of each to the whole system in which it plays a part. From what has already been said of "superior" children, it follows that they have an innate capacity for organization, greater than that of average children. Nevertheless this ability needs practice and cultivation. In the senior grades and in high school there are many children of superior ability who have never learned good habits of working or thinking, largely because of inadequate training. They have never, for example, formed the habit of

incorporating material from many sources into an integrated view of a topic.[1]

(6) The transfer of learning from one situation to another occurs easily in children with superior intelligence, chiefly because of the ability of these children to generalize and to see the broader significance of the topic at hand. This fact, however, as a basis for action, must be used with caution. Even with the very superior child, transfer of attitudes and abstract ideas will occur easily only when specifically provided for in the learning situation. The *habit* of applying to one field facts, methods, or ideas learned in another field is one that should be continuously developed in every school subject and situation. An interesting case in point is the transfer of the objective, scientific attitude from the school situation to the problems of human living.

(7) Superior children are unlikely to suffer much from arbitrary standards and set curriculums. They are able to do prescribed work satisfactorily with a minimum of effort. If they work reasonably well they usually obtain excellent grades and abundant praise from the teacher. As long as they continue to work acceptably and keep out of trouble, they cause the teacher no concern. It frequently happens that the teacher regards them merely as "average" pupils and does not give them a second thought. For these children a second thought is always advisable. Working with their slower classmates, superior children tend to become bored with school. Ennui, in turn, may lead some of them into mischief and antisocial

[1] Rachel Salisbury has an interesting workbook (*Better Work Habits in Composition,* Scott, Foresman and Company, 1935) which, although designed for high-school students, will be of help to teachers in developing such habits in the superior children of the elementary-school grades. See also Frederick, R. W., *How to Study Handbook,* D. Appleton-Century Company, Inc., New York, 1938.

behavior. The more common danger, however, is that they may develop poor habits of industry, perseverance, application, and concentration. To get the utmost out of school, they, like others, must learn to work and to achieve in proportion to their capacity.

III. THE EDUCATION OF SUPERIOR CHILDREN

The problems of grading and promotion will be discussed in a later chapter.[2] In the traditional school system, unless the child does so poorly in his schoolwork that he is required to spend two or three years in one grade, he advances one grade a year. Such a rigid system makes it difficult for gifted children to travel at a rate in keeping with their advancing mental ability. Too often these bright children, having the capacity of children a grade or two ahead of them, are kept in "lock step" with those who are average or dull. That they are not problems, just as frequently as dull children, who are forced to do work beyond their ability, is a credit to their general stability rather than to the educational system.

The question of speeding up their advance through school is one of primary importance. There is no simple solution. Generally speaking, it is not good practice, hygienically, for these children to "skip" several grades. If such a procedure were carried on logically there would be some children leaving elementary school at the age of ten or eleven. Occasionally, however, a double promotion is indicated. Usually it is advisable to effect this promotion in the earlier grades, for it is then easier from an administrative point of view.

As a rule, children in the gifted group should not enter high school before the age of thirteen, or twelve at the

[2] See page 210.

very earliest; otherwise they find themselves grouped with pupils physically and socially much more mature. The possible results of overacceleration are at least three: (1) the accelerated children are at a disadvantage in athletics and class games; (2) they are exposed to condescension on the part of the other pupils; and (3) they may be stimulated by the necessity of working and playing with a group older than themselves—with repercussions in terms of strain and nervous excitability. Even a moderate acceleration is open to these dangers. Occasionally one of these very bright children is encountered in a classroom with a few much older and retarded pupils. Sometimes such a child is selected for teasing and bullying. This sort of treatment is almost certain to breed feelings of insecurity, uneasiness, and inferiority. The result, in overcompensation of various sorts, may closely resemble the case of the retarded child in the reverse situation.[3]

Rather than accelerating a child's grade advancement, more constructive educational procedure is to focus the attention on enriching the curriculum and modifying the teaching methods. If the teacher has an intelligent grasp of the abilities and needs of bright children, he may easily so adapt their work that they will obtain legitimate satisfaction from it. The teacher using formal procedures must recognize that they need less drill than the average, and must not penalize them with extra review for getting their work done first. Standards of achievement commensurate with their ability should be maintained, and some enrichment of the curriculum provided where necessary. Respect for the personality of these "superior" children, resourcefulness on the part of the

[3] See page 118.

teacher, and some individualization of teaching and management will do much toward giving them the chance to develop their potentialities.

The fact that the teacher is in a rural school does not excuse him from making some effort to enrich the studies of this group. Most schools have some library equipment; and reading is an interest that can be developed. Even if library facilities are limited, there still remains for the rural teacher the abundance of free materials that can be supplied through travel agencies, tourist bureaus, railways, industrial firms, and the various departments of the Federal government. Many teachers, too, can secure from friends or interested organizations excellent magazines which would be of help. Hobbies and collections can be fostered, and special abilities in art or other fields developed. Extracurricular activities should be used fully.[4] More important still, there should be added training in responsibility, in organizing their own time, in initiating plans, in helping other pupils, and the like.

The foregoing suggestions are based on the assumption that the superior children remain in the regular class. In many schools, however, ability grouping of various kinds enables these children to be gathered together in classes by themselves; and, that being the case, enrichment can be carried out in greater detail. Ability-grouping that does not entail a modified curriculum is open to as many objections in the case of superior as in the case of borderline or dull normal children. Rapid progress

---

[4] Such activities as radio clubs, newspaper clubs, forestry clubs, arts and crafts clubs, and so on can be organized. (See Osburn and Rohan, *Enriching the Curriculum for Gifted Children.*) The "regular" school subjects can also be made more interesting for the children by systematic enrichment. (See Adams and Brown, *Teaching the Bright Pupil.*)

through the ordinary curriculum is unsuitable beyond the degree of acceleration discussed earlier in this section. The grouping of the superior children should be for the purpose of enrichment, not for acceleration.

IV. THE GENIUS

Once or twice in every teacher's lifetime a child is encountered who is so outstanding in his mental abilities, as well as in his temperament and personality, that a special challenge is presented. The education of these specially gifted children carries with it a particular responsibility to society. Much has been written about the conservation of our natural resources: the claims of forest, soil, and mine are advanced, and rightly so. But the greatest natural resource of any nation lies in its gifted individuals. To them it must look for leadership in government, literature, art, music, and in philanthropic and social progress. On them it must depend for invention, research, and discovery in the field of pure and applied science. While special abilities and training play their part in high achievement, they are quite inadequate as a means to creative and inventive progress unless they are supported by the very best in general intelligence. This is true in art, music, and literature just as much as in scientific research. Methods of work, habits of industry, perseverance, courage, fine social and emotional qualities, and other aspects of social adequacy and adaptability play a great part in outstanding achievement; but, in any field involving original creation, high general intelligence is the one indispensable factor.

To a considerable extent the attitude of society towards its gifted children has been one of waste. Inspirational and professional speakers frequently suggest that the gifted are quite capable of looking after themselves; and that, if they are really talented, they will climb to the top in spite of lack of opportunity. Such an attitude is similar to that of the farmer who neglects his prize-winning, pure-bred cow because she will give a reasonable amount of milk with a minimum of care. It is true that exceptionally bright children will do well; but the facts indicate that, because of faulty or inadequate development at school, many very gifted people fail to realize the goals which they are so well equipped to attain. This faulty development is not necessarily limited to the intellectual sphere: defects in the development of social and emotional habits are equally common.

The popular idea that the gifted child is puny, sickly, and queer has been shown to be entirely without foundation. Terman[5] found that gifted children are large and strong for their ages, healthier than average children, contribute far less than their quota to juvenile delinquency, and are more emotionally stable. He found also that these children are much more interested in play and have more "play knowledge" than the average child. They know more games of intellectual skill, such as bridge and chess, and are much less interested in aimless random play. Because gifted children are likely to be associated with children who are older chronologically and, therefore, possess greater physical strength, they often choose for outdoor sports those that depend chiefly on skill rather than on strength. They therefore often avoid football and Rugby, and may become greatly interested in swimming and tennis or in games like volleyball or basketball, where body-checking is not so promi-

[5] Terman, L. M., *Genetic Studies of Genius*, Volume I, Stanford University Press, Stanford University, California, 1926.

nent a feature. The general opinion that gifted children are not interested in outdoor sports is shown by investigation to be erroneous.

V. FAULTY PERSONALITY DEVELOPMENT AMONG SUPERIOR CHILDREN

Intelligence alone is no insurance against personal and emotional maladjustments. Indeed there are some who believe that the incidence of such problems increases as the intelligence level rises.[6] Certainly the fact that these children are very intelligent means that they appreciate, more quickly than the average, personal and social situations that form possible threats to their successful achievement. Their nervous systems are not necessarily more delicate than others, in the sense of being more liable to disorders, but their psychological constitution makes it possible for them to respond with finer and more delicate discriminations. Since, in this way, bright children are more sensitive to environmental forces, they must be guided in their development with special care.

Superior children are subject to the same thwartings and frustrations as other children. That they do not become maladjusted at school as frequently as retarded children may mean only that they have relatively fewer intellectual obstacles to meet. In other words, they find work in the ordinary grades very easy. In the tests and examinations they usually do well and receive praise and approbation. Hence, they have fewer reasons to develop feelings of inferiority. On the contrary, they expect to

[6] Levy, John, "A Quantitative Study of Relationship between Intelligence and Economic Status as Factors in the Etiology of Children's Behavior Problems," *American Journal of Orthopsychiatry*, I:52-62, January, 1931.

win, and perhaps are allowed to win too often and too easily for their own good.

In a previous paragraph it was explained how a too-rapid advance in school could have resultant difficulties in adjustment. More commonly, emotional maladjustment occurs as a result of situations arising in play and recreational groups during recess or outside of school altogether. Thus random play, which delights the "average" child until he is seven or eight years old, is usually disliked by the superior child. He becomes bored with just tossing a ball about, running and shouting, and even with slightly organized games like tag. He wants to organize the play into more complicated patterns and thus frequently becomes unpopular with the other children.

Deprived of social recreation, many gifted children develop solitary habits of play, indulge in elaborate mathematical reasonings, and are fond of collecting, reading, or games with imaginary playmates. Carried to extremes this sort of behavior does not make for healthy all-round development, and needs attention; but well-meaning efforts to "socialize" the child by trying to make him play games unsuited to him may do more harm than good. The solution to the problem, since it depends on the individual circumstances governing each particular case, is not always easy to find. In general terms, the solution is "enrichment of program," but the phrase should be interpreted to mean not merely more work, or more advanced work, but work that allows the child of superior intelligence to contribute to the social life of the whole group. Enterprise and activity programs symbolize this type of enrichment in healthful and practical ways.

Some of the problems of the superior child are well illustrated by the case of a girl almost thirteen years old who had a mental age of nearly seventeen and an I.Q. of 132. She was in Grade Nine. She presented no problem whatever to the school, but she was very much worried about herself. She had no friends and felt "left out of things." Her greatest wish was to be popular and to be a success at parties and other social events. She was failing miserably in this ambition; and the situation was rapidly becoming acute.

Starting school at six, she had been quickly promoted to Grade Two and had progressed steadily thereafter. She usually "came first" in her class, and her conduct was consistently excellent. She asked interesting and penetrating questions; but she was shy. Her home background was good. Her father was a hard-working, conscientious mechanic, interested in labor problems. Her mother was intelligent and understanding; and it was she who wanted her daughter examined. "She has an inferiority complex," the mother confided, "and it is taking all the joy out of her life. She seems actually to be afraid of her school friends; and she lacks confidence in everything she does." The child's physical and developmental history were normal.

More light was thrown on the problem by the girl herself in the interview. She stated, "The girls in the class don't like me. When they were picking a president they didn't even nominate me." Her chief occupations outside school were reading, listening to the radio, and going for long solitary walks. Her mother was her only companion.

It was easy to discuss the situation and the problem with the girl. She wanted to help herself, and was willing to follow suggestions in every detail. It was pointed out to her that although she was in Grade Nine most of the girls her own age were still in Grade Six or Grade Seven. Because of her academic success and solitary interests, her classmates regarded her as a "high-brow." The girls of her own grade had reached the "boy" stage and could think and talk of nothing but parties and dances. She was not interested in boys. As a matter of fact, the thought of "going out" with them frightened her a little. Furthermore, her vivid imagination magnified and exaggerated her problems for her. It was explained that, even if she did nothing, things would automatically right themselves in the course of two or three years. Meanwhile, the art of making friends by taking a genuine interest in others was discussed with her. She was given concrete tasks in making friendships and was asked to report the results each month.

VI. THE TEACHER AND THE SUPERIOR CHILD

The following paragraphs summarize those points most worthy of note in the education of superior and gifted children.

Special care should be taken to see that the educational program of such children is well balanced: intellectual, social, and emotional learning should all be taken into account. In every way possible, the creative abilities of the children should be developed. This particularly applies to social studies, art, music, literature, and dramatics. Every attempt should be made to build up a real background of experience which will contribute to organized creative thought.

The teacher should be sensitive to the importance of character training. Superior ability may be a detriment to society if moral integrity is not linked with it. The development of sound character cannot be achieved merely by appealing to feelings and emotions. Since superior children have the ability to think logically about problems of conduct, they should be guided towards the formulation of codes which further the welfare of society.

Character is inseparably related to personality; and as there is always a danger, especially in regular classes, that the bright child may become impatient with the slow thinker and feel himself definitely superior, it is particularly important that the teacher should encourage attitudes and habits of thinking that are definitely objective. In the classroom, opportunity must be provided for learning tolerance for the ideas of others and patience in waiting for one's turn to speak.

In a word, the superior child, like the dull child, presents problems in mental hygiene. These represent a challenge to good teaching and sound education.

REFERENCES

Adams, F., and Brown, W., *Teaching the Bright Pupil*, Henry Holt and Company, Inc., New York, 1930

Bentley, J. E., *Superior Children*, W. W. Norton & Company, Inc., New York; George J. McLeod, Ltd., Toronto, 1937

Hollingworth, L. A. S., *Gifted Children*, The Macmillan Company, New York, 1926

Louttit, C. M., *Clinical Psychology*, Harper & Brothers, New York; The Musson Book Company, Ltd., Toronto, 1936

Osburn, W. J., and Rohan, B. J., *Enriching the Curriculum for Gifted Children*, The Macmillan Company, New York, 1931

Stedman, L. M., *Education of Gifted Children*, World Book Company, Yonkers-on-Hudson, 1924

Teachers' Problems with Exceptional Children (11 Gifted Children), United States Office of Education, Pamphlet No. 41, Government Printing Office, Washington, D. C., 1933

A complete bibliography of studies dealing with the education and mental hygiene of the gifted child is contained in the *Journal of Exceptional Children*, January, 1938 (extra issue).

CHAPTER VII

PHYSICAL HANDICAPS

I. PERSONALITY DEVELOPMENT AND ORGANIC INFERIORITY

Nervousness, emotional instability, and other indexes of faulty personality development frequently arise in the child who is sensitive about an organic or physical defect. It is not intended that this chapter should deal specifically with the medical aspects of these problems. We are more interested in the effect of common physical disabilities on intellectual, social, and emotional development. Education cannot ignore the special needs of children with physical handicaps.

II. CRIPPLED CHILDREN [1]

For purposes of education the term "crippled children" includes those "whose muscular movements are restricted by disease, accident, or congenital deformities." [2] The number of crippled children attending school varies from time to time. Although available figures show that it rises as high as twenty-six per thousand, actually the number would be greater than this if all minor forms of disability were included.

While medical treatment will eventually restore some of these crippled children to normal health, the majority of them will have to go through life with their handicaps more or less unremedied. Their education, therefore,

[1] Part of the material in this section appeared in the *Special Class Teacher,* February, 1938, and is reproduced here by permission.
[2] *Crippled Children in Chicago,* a survey made for the Rotary Club of Chicago, The Chicago Community Trust, 1924.

gives rise to special problems. Vocational training, occupational therapy, and personal hygiene must go hand in hand with academic instruction and are most effectively correlated in schools provided with special facilities and staff. Several of the larger cities have special schools for crippled children and children with other physical defects. Usually it is necessary to provide busses in order to take such children to and from school. In many cities the more seriously affected children are taught in their own homes by visiting teachers, co-operating with the health authorities or family physician.

However, we are more concerned here with the crippled children who are attending the regular schools. Although most of them have normal or superior intelligence and should, like other children, be placed in regular classes at a level appropriate to their mental age, they usually do require special consideration. Special desk accommodation may be necessary.[3] Other equipment may include large, soft-leaded pencils for children whose finer co-ordinated movements are poor. Large sheets of paper on which to draw and write are also useful. The curriculum should be diversified in order to emphasize not only academic work but also handicraft and practical and vocational work. Academic training should, of course, include the fundamental skills. For the child who is frequently absent for special treatment, it may be necessary to reorganize the schoolwork and time-table so that he may derive as much benefit as possible from his attendance at school. As a general rule, each crippled child should be thought of as an educational

[3] Desks such as the Elgin adjustable desk, the Rowles movable study desk, and the American Universal desk are suitable. Details can be obtained from dealers.

problem in himself and given as much individual attention as is practical.

The medical care and treatment of children with such difficulties will often require the co-operation of the teacher and the school. Frequently the teacher is in a unique position to help in the re-education of weak muscles. The strength of finger movements can be helped by their use in modeling with plasticine or even by placing checkers in the spaces of a checkerboard; but such procedures should be discussed in detail with the physician or the physiotherapist. The teacher should certainly not assume by himself the full responsibility for such re-education.

Children who are crippled as the result of disasters like poliomyelitis or birth injury may suffer from obscure difficulties. The damage to the central nervous system may not be limited to those parts controlling the movement of the limbs. Sometimes there has been involvement of that part which has to do with emotional control; and, as a result, the children so affected are emotionally unstable, irritable, excitable, and hard to manage. In addition to the direct physical cause of personality difficulties, crippled children often suffer from overprotection and spoiling at home. In cases of poliomyelitis, where there has been a long convalescence, for example, parental oversolicitation, unwise sympathy, and too much attention almost invariably occur.

As a result of one or more of these factors certain personality traits are characteristic. These children may cry easily, laugh excessively, or fall into angry tantrums. Their attention span may be short, and they may have more than average difficulty in concentration. No matter how these problems arise, the teacher must take them into account in arranging the work. Too long a spell of one kind of activity may lead to signs of boredom, fatigue, or frank emotional outbursts. If emotional episodes do occur, what should the teacher do? This is a difficult problem, because a crippled child cannot be dealt with in the way that one would deal with a normal healthy child. Should the teacher allow the child complete freedom to do as he likes, so that frustration, anger, and tears simply do not appear? Or should he "clamp down" on this infantile behavior and scold the child for his emotional display? Probably the answer is, "Neither the one nor the other." After all, the child has probably been raised in a sheltered environment. In the case of a crippling illness, such as poliomyelitis or bone tuberculosis, he will have been out of school for a long time. He must be given an opportunity to learn to adjust himself to the classroom requirements. Patience and understanding, certainly, will be required. Gradually he must be made to realize that he has increasing responsibilities in the matter of self-control. It may take several months for him to learn this control, but he can be helped by encouragement and reassurance from the teacher.

This leads us to one of the most important aspects of the whole educational problem for crippled children. Because of the dramatic nature of their disability and the slowness with which they improve, the children may develop many undesirable attitudes toward themselves, toward authority, and, especially, toward work. The defeatist attitude of the chronically ill, extreme selfishness, expectation and demand for help in even the simplest tasks, and lazy habits of work will frequently be found. No matter how much we may sympathize with the child in his illness, we must never let this sympathy be detrimental to his mental and social development. We cannot afford to have mental as well as physical cripples in our schools. For this reason the teacher must try to combine the necessary protection against fatigue with a healthy objectivity and a gentle firmness in respect to conformity to the essentials in routine.

Social activities are extremely important. Considerable skill and tact are necessary to assist the child in developing a sense of adequate security. He tends to become oversensitive and to feel inadequate and inferior. Often this feeling is aggravated by teasing and ridiculing on the part of other children. The teacher must endeavor to foresee and prevent the occurrence of situations which might break down his morale. He should not be ignored, slighted, or kept out of social activity, but should enter, as fully as possible, into group projects and those extracurricular and extraclassroom activities which are not too exciting or fatiguing. The other children of the class, under good guidance, can be of great assistance here. Encouraged by the teacher, they will think of ways of including him in their schemes. By these means the child can be helped to face his difficulty objectively and to face the future cheerfully with confidence and optimism.

Vocational activity is another aspect of the teacher's task of guidance. Crippled children should be allowed to start, as soon as feasible, those activities which may, in the future, contribute to their support. Interest can easily be stimulated in activities such as woodworking, stenography, writing, printing, or proofreading. The nature of the activity chosen depends on the nature of the child's disability; and care must be taken to help the child find a field of endeavor in which he has a chance to succeed. There is one danger, however, that must be carefully avoided. Too often these children, through the optimistic attitudes and encouragement of enthusiastic teachers, come to feel that they can get a job and be completely self-supporting. While in some cases this is true, most of the children who are badly crippled must eventually be content with employment in some sheltered workshop or in their own home; and this is often disappointing in its remuneration. It is a mistake, therefore, to raise hopes of employment and economic independence too high. The subsequent disillusionment and disappointment may be very painful. It is far sounder mental hygiene to encourage these activities as interests and hobbies in the way one encourages literature and creative art.

The kind of social and emotional difficulties encountered by crippled children, and the results of two contrasting methods of dealing with them, are illustrated by the following account of two boys:

One was born with a clubfoot. His mother never quite forgave him for this, and would frequently speak disparagingly of him. At school he was teased and shunned. At first he was extremely sensitive and frequently tearful about the situation, but as time went on his attitude to others and his whole mental outlook changed. He became obstinate and stubborn, and developed a very bad temper. He took refuge in the fact that the other children hesitated to hit him back in the fights which he started. Everyone in the neighborhood knew him as "that crippled brat."

The other boy was lame in both legs from poliomyelitis, which he had contracted in an epidemic when he was three. From the beginning his parents treated his difficulty in a very matter-of-fact manner. By wise unemotional upbringing, they were able to prevent him from developing any self-pity. The teachers at school co-operated. He entered into school athletics by being, first, the mascot and then the manager of the hockey teams. He is now at a university, making a name for himself in economics. His attitudes towards himself and society are thoroughly healthy and normal, and he is one of the most popular boys in his year.

III. CHILDREN WITH SPEECH DEFECTS

Speech may be defined as bodily activity resulting in the production of articulate sounds which are conventionally accepted and understood as symbols by which people may communicate ideas to one another. Defects in speech occur frequently and are of many varieties. Surveys place the incidence at between 3% and 5% of the school population. In large centers the most serious cases are grouped together for special training under special teachers. However, there are usually one or two left over in each class, and these are the responsibility of the regular teacher.

It is not our purpose to give detailed instructions concerning the management and correction of such speech defects. We wish only to present their mental-hygiene significance. As various types of defects, however, imply different types of mental-hygiene problems, a simple classification is necessary.

There are four typical kinds of speech disorder.[4] In order of frequency of occurrence they are: (1) articulatory defects; (2) stuttering and stammering; (3) delayed speech; and (4) disorders of voice. Stuttering, like some other nervous tics and habits, is usually considered a symptom of poor emotional development rather than a

[4] A more comprehensive classification of disorders of speech is contained in *A Dictionary of Terms Dealing with Disorders of Speech*, compiled by S. D. Robbins and S. M. Stinchfield, American Society for the Study of Disorders of Speech, Boston, 1931.

physical defect. For this reason it was dealt with separately.[5]

(1) *Articulatory defects*. This group includes lisping, sound substitutions, "cluttering," speech clumsiness, and similar disorders. The cause of the defect is frequently a physical abnormality. Harelip, cleft palate, high or low palatal arch, unnatural set of the jaws, irregularities of the teeth, thick, sluggish tongue, paralysis of the facial muscles or the other organs of speech, and large adenoidal growths are examples of such physical factors. Many of these are remediable either by adequate medical treatment or by proper exercises and training.

Even where there is no discoverable deformity or physical defect, the treatment of articulatory disorder should consist of exercises and ear training. The exercises are many and varied and are devised to develop control of the jaws, lips, tongue, and palate. Simple examples will be found in the references listed at the end of this chapter.

Ear training is especially important, because the child learns speech by hearing and by imitating. For this reason he should hear good examples of well-articulated speech. A teacher whose speech is awkward, unpleasant, or defective cannot hope to have her pupils develop good speech habits. Practice and exercise in listening, trying out various positions of special organs, and attempting to imitate sounds are all valuable. From this it follows that the child who is partially deaf is unusually handicapped in his ability to learn good speech habits.

Any good speech teacher will acknowledge the importance of mental-hygiene principles in handling children with such defects. In the first place, it is practically

[5] See page 63.

impossible to re-educate such children if emotional factors are disregarded. An atmosphere of quiet and ease should be established. All hurry, worry, and tension, whether physical or mental, should be reduced to a minimum. Physical relaxation can be learned through practice. Lying down is a good way to begin. Mental and emotional ease come automatically when worries go; and confidence is built up by constant encouragement and reassurance. In speech training, especially, short periods of instruction are desirable. Long periods lead to fatigue; fatigue leads to muscular and emotional tension; and then good speech is impossible.

Just as the crippled child is likely to develop personality maladjustments unless the situation is carefully handled, so the child with articulatory speech defects may acquire faulty habits of thinking, feeling, and acting if he is not given guidance and help.

(2) *Delayed speech.* Children normally learn to talk during the first two years of life. Sometimes, however, speech is delayed, and the child does not talk until he is four, five, or even six years old. As a physical handicap deafness may sometimes be found as a cause of delayed speech; the teacher must be careful not to diagnose as feeble-minded a child who is suffering only from poor hearing. We mention deafness here as an instance of speech defect due to physical handicaps, but shall deal with deafness more fully later in the chapter. At this point, we may mention other causes of delayed speech. By far the most common cause of delayed speech, but by no means the only one, is feeble-mindedness. If a child of four or five years of age does not talk, or is just beginning to talk, an attempt should be made to secure an estimate of his mental ability and intellectual

development. For this purpose special non-language (performance) tests can be used. Still another cause is fear. Cases are on record in which a child started to talk at the normal age and was badly frightened by an accident or some other occurrence, and then did not, or could not, talk for months. Delayed speech may also occur through the lack of a stimulating environment, where the child learns very little speech or finds all his needs and desires granted *without* speech. Twins are usually slow in talking because they tend to develop a means of mutual communication through gestures and sounds that are meaningless to others. This private method of communication is sometimes sufficient for their needs, until they are three or four years of age.

(3) *Disorders of voice.* In order to complete the classification of speech defects, we refer to the many children whose chief difficulty has to do with the voice and sound production. Such disorders include huskiness, nasality, shrillness, weakness, loudness, and monotony. The causes of these disorders may be physical or psychological. Thus infection and swelling of the organs of speech, for example, makes the voice hoarse or even makes it impossible for the child to speak above a whisper. Nasal speech may be caused by obstruction due to adenoids. These are matters for the physician to investigate. If, however, the disorder arises from faulty habit formation, re-education is necessary. Many weak, timid, and almost inaudible voices are manifestations of the withdrawing type of personality; and this fundamental maladjustment must be treated before real progress can be made in teaching good speech habits.

IV. CHILDREN WITH SENSORY DEFECTS

The child who cannot sense or perceive the ordinary stimuli of light and sound is indeed handicapped. Obviously an educational problem, he also presents special psychological problems of adjustment and development, which are of tremendous importance to the teacher and to himself. The basic cause of defective vision or hearing is, in most cases, physical damage to the tissues involved. The treatment should always be in the hands of the physician and the nurse. The teacher has responsibilities, however. It is frequently his task to discover the presence of such defects and to see that treatment is carried out.

Defective Vision. Faulty vision seriously affects the child's learning capacity. It has been estimated that as many as 12% to 15% of all school children are unable to see clearly enough to succeed at everyday tasks in school. Although it is not our purpose to deal at length with the problems arising in educating these children, we may point out that every teacher should be able to discover such children when they appear in his classes. Children who are totally blind are usually excluded from the regular schools and educated in special institutions; but children having every variety of visual defect, from slight eyestrain to very low visual acuity are frequently concentrated in regular classrooms. Therefore it is important for the teacher to be able to recognize the chief signs of strain. These are: headache, irritability, holding the work too close to the eyes, strabismus (cross-eyes), inflammation of the whites of the eyes and eyelids, a tense facial expression, and a blinking, squinting, or "screwing-up" of the eyelids when trying to see small print or to read what is written on the blackboard. The diagnosis of defective vision should be verified by a visual test. If the teacher finds he has no available medical assistance, he can give a test himself by using one of the recognized testing charts.[6] Generally speaking, children who show such signs of eyestrain or who have a visual acuity demonstrably less than that of the other children in the class should see an oculist. They should be wearing properly fitted glasses. It is particularly important for children with "crossed eyes" to see an oculist as soon as possible. Newer methods of treatment are successful in correcting this disfiguring condition if begun early.

After measures have been taken to safeguard the eyes of children with normal sight and of those with minor visual defects, there remains another group of children with serious eye troubles who, even after proper treatment, cannot profitably be educated in the ordinary classroom. This group includes children with serious and progressive eye diseases and others who, although not blind, cannot read ordinary print and blackboard writing or

[6] The Snellen Chart, for example, is excellent for general purposes and can be obtained from any optical supply house for a few cents. Full instructions for the use of this chart are contained in any general reference on the health of school children or on clinical methods. (See *Clinical Psychology* by C. M. Louttit, page 570.)

A rough test of visual acuity can be given by the teacher if the child is old enough to recognize letters quickly and easily. Procure an ordinary children's book (such as a primer) in which the type is heavy, distinct, and quite large. Fasten this book on the wall at about the level of the children's eyes so that it can be opened at any page. Make sure that the book is very well illuminated. Then, if you are sure your own eyesight is normal, find the place farthest from the book at which you can just make out the letters. A good plan is to start fifteen or twenty feet from the book and advance very slowly. Mark the point on the floor from which the letters and words can first be distinguished. Check this point repeatedly by yourself and with the help of the other children. Then have the child you wish to test carry out the procedure, first with one eye covered, then with the other eye covered, and then using both eyes together. If the child obviously has difficulty seeing the letters, he should be referred to the family doctor or the oculist for expert examination.

can do so only at the expense of general health. These children really need the advantages of a sight-saving class. Indeed the National Committee for the Prevention of Blindness claims that one child in every five hundred of the school population requires special educational arrangements of this kind.[7]

However, since many children who need this service will, for the time being, have to remain in the regular classrooms, a brief account of the more usual sight-saving devices must be given. For a child requiring sight-saving attention the most essential requirement is light. He should be placed where he has continuous light of the greatest intensity and least possible glare. Direct sunlight, because of its glare, is not good light. Adjustable desks with a dull finish are helpful in overcoming glare. A small table and chair suitable to the size of the child serve the purpose very well. They can be moved about so as to keep the child in the best available light throughout the day. Other special equipment, as simple or elaborate as school finances permit, can be obtained from supply houses. It ranges all the way from pencils with soft, thick leads and unglazed paper in large sheets to specially made typewriters with extra large type. A child with a severe visual defect should be allowed to go as close to the blackboard, charts, or maps as he wishes.

The problem of helping such a child accept his affliction without feelings of inferiority or frustration is similar to that of the education of a crippled child. An objective, kindly attitude on the part of the teacher and a friendly uncritical welcome from the other children will help him

---

[7] *Sight-saving Classes—Their Organization and Administration,* Publication No. 30, National Society for the Prevention of Blindness, New York, 1937.

to attain a sense of security and happiness, especially if he is given an opportunity to contribute his share to the group activities of the class. As with the other handicapped children, vocational guidance consists in helping the child to discover some interest or task in which he has a fair chance of success without further endangering his vision. It is amazing how accomplished children who are almost totally blind can become, especially in such things as typing, broommaking, and basketweaving. These children sometimes make *faster* progress when they are encouraged to behave as if they were totally blind. This is because of the saving in strain and energy hitherto wasted in their efforts to see.

Defective Hearing. For the school child good hearing is only second in importance to good sight. It has been calculated that from 1% to 3% of all school children are seriously deficient in auditory acuity; [8] but careful surveys made with the help of audiometers have shown that from 8% to 15% of the children have defective hearing in one or both ears. In the average class of 35 to 40 pupils, therefore, the teacher can expect to find three or four children with hearing defective in some degree. One of these children is likely to have serious difficulty in hearing the teacher speak.

The early signs of faulty hearing in a child are fairly obvious. He will be continually asking the teacher to repeat words; he will turn his head in order to catch what was said, perhaps showing a strained facial expression; and sometimes he will complain of noises in his head. Such symptoms as earache or discharging ears are not, in themselves, indicative of deafness. Continued deaf-

---

[8] In the Saskatchewan survey, mentioned on page 90, only 1% of the children were found to have grossly defective hearing.

ness may eventually lead to unusual mistakes in speaking, peculiar qualities of the voice, and even to listlessness and inattention. Children suspected of being deaf should be referred to the nurse or doctor for examination. If medical services are not available, the teacher himself can make a rough estimate by testing the child's ability to hear a whisper or the ticking of a watch.[9] Children who are completely deaf should not be required to remain in the regular classroom. As is the case for the blind, institutions are available for their education in most states and provinces. The larger cities have special classes for the "hard-of-hearing," where lip reading is taught. The special arrangements and instruction required for such children need not concern us here. However, many teachers, especially in the more remote areas, have to deal with deaf or slightly deaf children by themselves. There are many simple things that can be done to help such children. In the first place, a child who is "hard of

[9] The "watch test" is very simple to perform. First have the child close one ear by placing the flat of his palm tightly against it. His eyes should be blindfolded or screened. Hold the watch to the other ear, making sure he can hear the ticking clearly. Then move it away slowly in a direct line from the ear. Have the child indicate the moment at which he can no longer hear it; and note this distance in inches. Move it back again toward the ear, asking the child to state the exact instant at which he begins to hear it again. The mean of these two distances is the figure desired. It is best to check this figure several times with each ear and then compare the resulting figure with those obtained similarly, using yourself and the other children as subjects. Watch ticks vary in intensity; but, when the room is quite silent, a large, well-made watch (not a wrist watch) can be heard six or eight feet from the ear.

The whisper test is much less accurate, but it is useful because it can be performed so quickly. Have the child close one ear as before; and, standing about twenty feet away, with the child's back to you, begin whispering numbers or the names of cities. The child must repeat what he hears. Whispers vary from time to time, even with the same individual. However, if the ordinary whispered voice cannot be heard at six feet, then there is no doubt that the child is deaf. The watch test and the whisper test, as well as more accurate methods of testing hearing acuity, are fully described in such books as *The Hygiene of the School Child* by Terman and Almack, or *Clinical Psychology* by Louttit.

hearing" should be seated in the second or third seat from the front in the row nearest the windows. Here he can hear the teacher's voice to the best advantage. In this position he can also hear more of what is said by the children in the class; and he is in a position to receive individual help from the teacher. Because such a child is likely to slip into lax methods of speaking, he should be given opportunity to express himself in carefully articulated speech. A mechanical aid to hearing, if available, should be freely used. Sometimes such an instrument makes a great difference to the child; and if he finds it helpful, he should become accustomed to it early.

Special attention should be given to the developing personality of these "hard-of-hearing" children. As a group, they are placed in an even more difficult position than the crippled or the blind. The latter defects are readily recognized by other people, and allowances are usually made for them; but the handicap of the deaf child is likely to go unrecognized. To avoid embarrassing situations, he will tend to withdraw from the group and to develop a feeling of timidity and inferiority. He becomes increasingly shy and often shows spells of irritability and emotional instability. Since he cannot hear what other people say, he may imagine that they are criticizing him, discussing his defect, or making fun of him. As a result, he may become suspicious and resentful. The teacher should proceed very carefully in dealing with such a child. He should neither pamper nor remind him constantly of his difficulty, but rather should encourage him to ignore it through participation in healthful group activities.

Deaf and partially deaf children need special help and guidance in the selection of a vocation. A decision will depend on the degree of deafness as well as on the opportunities which the local community affords. For very deaf boys such occupations as shoe repairing, barbering, and farm or factory work are suitable. For girls, laundry work, domestic work, filing work (in an office where answering a telephone is not involved), and certain kinds of library work are recommended. With adequate mechanical aids or with training in lip reading these children may not have to be considered as handicapped in any way.

V. CHILDREN SUFFERING FROM MALNUTRITION

Children who are badly nourished include not only those who are undernourished, but those whose diet has been inadequate in terms of the basic food requirements (including the necessary minerals and vitamins). Malnourished children, like sickly children, cannot be expected to receive the maximum benefit even from the most efficient teaching. A vigorous, well-nourished body is necessary not only for learning, but for every aspect —intellectual, emotional, and social—of the child's development.

In diagnosing malnutrition, height-weight tables must be used with caution. Extreme deviation from such standards is doubtless important; but it must be interpreted in the light of the clinical data collected in each case. The typical undernourished child is likely to be thin, pale, with almost transparent skin and a sallow or pasty complexion. His muscles are underdeveloped and flabby; his posture is usually poor. He seems constantly tired and listless; and he is frequently dubbed "lazy." Another type, however, is restless, high-strung, and irritable, lacks physical and mental endurance, and cannot give concentrated attention to any one thing for more than a minute or two at a time. In either case, because of failing interest and lack of ability in schoolwork, the general impression is that the level of intelligence is falling. Actually there is little evidence to support the notion that malnutrition affects general intelligence in any way whatever. It is therefore unlikely that the removal of the symptoms of malnutrition will appreciably raise the I.Q. of a child.

Occasionally the malnutrition may take the form of extreme obesity. The factors producing such an increase in weight, however, are only rarely related to food or health habits. More often the essential cause of the difficulty is a constitutional or glandular disturbance. This type of physical handicap is considered in more detail later.[10]

When a teacher suspects that a child is suffering from malnutrition he should report him to the school nurse or doctor. If the doctor agrees with the teacher, there is much that the latter can do to help remedy the situation. In so far as malnutrition is the result of physical disease, specific treatment must naturally be left to the doctor. The teacher can co-operate by reducing the amount of school pressure and strain and by determining whether the child requires any special attention concerning his grading and the method of instruction in the classroom. He may require individual help in certain subjects, for example. Furthermore, the teacher can often help the doctor in educating the parents so as to alter the health habits of the home. The fatiguing effects of adult social activities connected with the home, especially those which defer the normal bedtime, should be explained. Abundant

[10] See page 173.

fresh air, a good diet, sufficient rest and sleep, and an adequate amount of exercise and play are essential. Sometimes the teacher can persuade public-spirited philanthropists or service clubs to supply milk to these malnourished children during school hours.[11]

VI. CHILDREN WITH OTHER PHYSICAL HANDICAPS

Chronic Illnesses. Closely related to children who are malnourished are those who are suffering from some long standing toxic or infectious condition. These children are being slowly poisoned. The poison may be a toxic substance taken into the body by accident (by contaminated food, for example), or it may be a toxic substance manufactured in the body as a result of bacterial infection. The latter condition, of course, is much more common. Such chronic infection (sometimes called *autointoxication*) may result from infected tonsils or low-grade infections in other parts of the body (sinuses, appendix, and so on). In this group also must be included children who are suffering from tuberculosis and heart disease.

Children suffering from such chronic conditions are similar in appearance to those described in the previous section. Characteristically, they have low vitality, poor color, and are easily fatigued. The condition may arise so gradually that the teacher may not realize that anything is seriously wrong. The following case summary illustrates this type of difficulty:

A boy of nine, in Grade Three, was falling behind in his schoolwork. Except for this he presented no particular problem. His intelligence was a little better than average, but his

[11] The importance of an adequate amount of milk in the diet of growing children cannot be overemphasized. A school-aged child should drink from a pint to a quart of milk a day in order to ensure adequate supplies of calcium, iron, and vitamins.

interest in work was lagging; and he was putting forth poor effort. The teacher noticed that he had a pale and wan appearance and that he frequently complained of being "too tired to play." As a consequence, he tended to keep to himself a good deal. The teacher discussed this boy with the inspector, and on the latter's recommendation she arranged for the child to be given a physical examination by the school doctor. The doctor discovered that the boy was suffering from the effects of a long-standing intoxication from chronically diseased tonsils. This condition had been diagnosed when the boy had had his first physical examination at the age of six. Treatment had been recommended then but had not been carried out. The physical results of this chronic infection were briefly stated by the physician as anemia, weakness, and lassitude. Following adequate surgical and medical treatment the boy's health improved. He gained in weight, his color improved, and he became more vigorous. A summer at camp re-established his social interests; and by autumn he was once more doing good work at school.

The children who are suffering from prolonged illnesses, such as tuberculosis, will usually not be the immediate concern of the teacher. Such children should be properly cared for at a suitable hospital or sanatorium. There are children, however, who, while not suffering from active tubercular lesions, have been exposed to tubercular infection and, because of lowered vitality or malnutrition, are considered to be likely candidates for the disease. Still others have had mild tubercular infections but have recovered.

Every large municipality has special educational facilities for these children. The treatment consists of open-air classes, where steps are taken to provide facilities for added rest and nourishment in addition to the greatest possible amount of sunshine and fresh air. Some of these classes are held in city parks and are open most of the summer or during the fine weather. Such classes are beneficial to all children who are physically below normal and undernourished. With these children the educational objective is good health, which means, in terms of mental hygiene, that they should be encouraged to regard the future fearlessly. Feelings of inferiority, dependence upon others, and too great a consciousness of their own precarious health should be discouraged.

The acute infections such as measles and scarlet fever are not likely to cause such difficulties, since children suffering from this type of illness are too ill to come to school. The problem of their convalescence, however, is one that may affect the teacher. Sometimes the children are back at school before they are fully recovered from the effects of these acute childhood diseases. During this convalescent period they must be regarded as being physically handicapped in precisely the same way as children who are recovering from poliomyelitis. Their prolonged stay at home under the care of worried parents may have established bad emotional habits and feelings of dependency. In such cases, the teacher should arrange the classroom situation so that the child gradually becomes accustomed again to the intellectual and social activities of school life. The dangers of prolonged spoiling and pampering are very real.

The number of school children suffering from an active or incipient form of heart trouble is astonishingly large. It is estimated that nearly 2% of the school population has some cardiac disease; and nearly one third of these is seriously disabled thereby. These children need a great deal of careful guidance by their teachers if they are to attain anything like wholesome development. Their movements and activities are sometimes so restricted that normal social and emotional contact with their fellow pupils is impossible. Yet, unlike the crippled and the blind, they do not, on most occasions, give apparent signs of their need for special consideration; nor can they themselves, as it often happens, be brought to understand why such great care is imperative. Careful explanations coupled with "moral support" and encouragement will usually enable them to make a satisfactory adjustment. Unfortunately, many of them must look forward to a sheltered life and very limited opportunities for active useful employment.

Epilepsy. Among the group of specially handicapped children there are none who create more problems or demand more careful attention than those who suffer from epileptic fits or convulsions. Such children are not commonly encountered. It has been estimated that the incidence is about one in a thousand of the school population.[12] Epileptic children may be normal, apart from their fits. Some of them, however, have difficult personalities and require special attention. The relationship of epilepsy to retardation is still a matter for debate. The incidence of feeble-mindedness among epileptics is certainly higher than in normal groups. But, on the other hand, extremely high intelligence is also found in some of them, a fact too often overlooked.

The epileptic child tends to worry about his condition. He may be extremely sensitive and feel that he is different from other children. His real or imagined stigmata may make his task of adjusting to his situation difficult.

---

[12] The characteristics of a true epileptic fit and the emergency measures which the teacher should be responsible for are described in detail in such books as Louttit's *Clinical Psychology* (page 612).

Just as the crippled child or the child who has limited intelligence may overcompensate in ways that are not socially acceptable, so the epileptic, in his attempt to gain security, may become a behavior problem. The mental-hygiene principles to be remembered are not different from those which are already familiar to the teacher. The child should be made to realize that he is definitely one of the class, and that he has, therefore, responsibilities in the same way as the other children. There is no point in stressing the fact that he is different from the others; nor need the teacher feel apprehensive concerning the convulsions. If proper medical care has been instituted, it is quite unlikely that seizures will take place during the school day.

The question of a suitable vocation may be difficult to solve. Many occupations are naturally closed to epileptics. For instance, it is dangerous for them to drive cars or trucks. Usually some clerical or other sedentary occupation will be most likely to prove satisfactory.

Endocrine Disturbances. In any large school there will be found some children who are suffering from glandular disorder. This may take one of several forms. The endocrine glands are responsible for the control of such vital functions as growth, sexual development, the rate at which we utilize food and manufacture energy, and the degree to which we are capable of becoming emotionally excited. Consequently disturbances in the function of one of these glands may have catastrophic effects on the developing personality.

The following case is an excellent example of the kind of difficulty encountered by a child whose pituitary gland was not functioning properly. A thirteen-year-old boy weighed 185 pounds. Although his I.Q. was 122 and he was in Grade Nine, he was finally referred to the mental-hygiene clinic because of persistent truancy. On examining him, the doctor found many defects more serious than truancy. He had, for instance, a very marked stammer, concerning which (as with his obesity) he was extremely sensitive. Two years previously he had been sent to a boys' camp, where, as a result of homesickness, self-consciousness, and timidity, he became morose and unhappy and had finally developed a fever which made it necessary for him to go home. The immediate cause of his truancy was the fact that, during his physical-training periods, when his obesity became more apparent in the gymnasium uniform, the other boys teased him mercilessly. He avoided this discomfiture by staying away from school on physical-training days. Gradually the teasing carried over into the academic and other school periods.

The boy's school history showed that, although he had had a double promotion early in his career, he had, nevertheless, regarded school merely as a necessary form of annoyance. As he had developed no real interests in schoolwork, there was nothing there to compensate him for the stigma of being obese. He had a decided preference for those teachers who left him completely alone or, at any rate, did not render him conspicuous by forcing him to take an active part in classroom procedures. Out of school he was a solitary, seclusive child, with only one friend, an aggressive, feeble-minded boy of his own age. His only interest was to bicycle through the streets by himself or with his friend.

A good teacher in the early grades, when the problem of obesity was just beginning, could have helped this boy greatly, both in his attitude toward his weight and with his stammer. Several interviews with the psychologist helped the child to understand his difficulties and to face them frankly and objectively. This particular boy, in addition, was greatly helped by suitable treatment with glandular extracts.

Generally speaking, there is no direct or quantitative relation between the seriousness of a physical handicap and its effect on mental health. On the contrary, maladjustment, even in extremes, may be caused by quite minor defects of the more apparent kind. Thus skin blemishes (birthmarks, moles, scars, and so on) and, to a lesser degree, facial irregularities (crossed eyes, prominent teeth, and so forth) may cause intense unhappiness and feelings of inferiority, especially in girls. Once certain that such a defect cannot be remedied, the teacher should appeal to the child's common sense and direct his energies from useless self-pity into constructive activity.

VII. HYSTERICAL ILLNESSES

This chapter would be incomplete without some reference to those children who react to difficulties by a conscious or unconscious imitation of various types of physical ailments. These ailments, psychologically induced, may be of the most amazing and dramatic type. Hysterical blindness and deafness have been observed in children. Various kinds of limps are displayed—some of them quite bizarre and unlike anything ever produced by organic disease. Sometimes hysterical faints and even "convulsions" occur.[13] This usually happens when a child, especially susceptible to suggestion, observes someone else in a real convulsion. These so-called hysterical paralyses, faints, and fits are often difficult for even the expert to diagnose with certainty. The teacher should never take the responsibility of deciding between a real and a hysterical condition, unless the ailment has been so obviously suggested by recent events that there is no possibility of doubt. The important point is that hyster-

[13] See, for instance, the case illustration on page 62.

ical children are usually not just dissembling. They themselves believe in the realness of their illness and cannot put it aside by an act of will. Hysterical maladies can usually be cured by a physician through the use of powerful suggestion. However, unless the underlying cause for this form of maladjustment be discovered and eliminated, these children will be subject to a recurrence of the same or similar symptoms. It is cases of this sort that swell the "perfect cure" list of quacks and other irregular practitioners.

REFERENCES

For further suggestions as to the education and mental hygiene of children with physical disabilities, the teacher is referred to the following:

(A) *Crippled Children*

> Abt, H. E., *The Care, Cure and Education of the Crippled Child*, International Society for Crippled Children, Elyria, Ohio, 1924

> Berry, C. S., "The Exceptional Child in Regular Classes," *Journal of Exceptional Children*, III:15-16, October, 1936

> *Care and Education of Crippled Children*, Wisconsin State Department of Public Instruction, Bulletin No. 1, Madison, Wisconsin, 1933

> Heck, A. O., *The Education of Crippled Children*, United States Office of Education, Bulletin No. 11, Government Printing Office, Washington, D. C., 1930

> Lemmen, O. L., *The Organization of Special Classes for Crippled Children*, University of the State of New York, Bulletin No. 995, Albany, New York, 1932

Martens, E. H., *Parents' Problems with Exceptional Children,* United States Office of Education, Bulletin No. 14, Government Printing Office, Washington, D. C., 1932

Teachers' Problems with Exceptional Children, V—Crippled Children, United States Office of Education, Bulletin No. 14, Government Printing Office, Washington, D. C., 1934

(B) *Speech Defects*

Case, I. M., and Barrows, S. T., *Speech Drills for Children in Form of Play,* Expression Company, Boston, 1929

Peppard, H. M., *The Correction of Speech Defects,* The Macmillan Company, New York, 1925

Speech Defects and Their Correction, United States Office of Education, Pamphlet No. 22, Government Printing Office, Washington, D. C.

The Speech-defective School Child, United States Office of Education, Bulletin No. 7, Government Printing Office, Washington, D. C., 1931

Van Thal, J. H., *Cleft Palate Speech,* George Allen & Unwin, Ltd., London, 1934

Wood, A. L., *The Jingle Book for Speech Correction,* E. P. Dutton & Co., Inc., New York, 1934

(C) *Defective Vision*

Schools and Classes for the Blind, United States Office of Education, Bulletin No. 9, Government Printing Office, Washington, D. C., 1928

Sight-saving Classes—Their Organization and Administration, Publication No. 30, The National Society for the Prevention of Blindness, Inc., New York, 1927

Teachers' Problems with Exceptional Children—I (Blind and Partially Seeing Children), United States Office of Education, Pamphlet No. 40, Government Printing Office, Washington, D. C., 1933

(D) *Defective Hearing*

Habbe, S., *Personality Adjustments of Adolescent Boys with Impaired Hearing,* Teachers College Contributions to Education, No. 697, Bureau of Publications, Teachers College, Columbia University, New York, 1936

Madden, R., *The School Status of the Hard-of-hearing Child,* Teachers College Contributions to Education, No. 499, Bureau of Publications, Teachers College, Columbia University, New York, 1931

Teachers' Problems with Exceptional Children—IV (Deaf and Hard-of-hearing Children), United States Office of Education, Pamphlet No. 54, Government Printing Office, Washington, D. C., 1934

The Deaf and the Hard-of-hearing in the Occupational World, United States Office of Education, Bulletin No. 13, Government Printing Office, Washington, D. C., 1936

(E) *Malnutrition*

Schools and Classes for Delicate Children, United States Office of Education, Bulletin No. 22, Government Printing Office, Washington, D. C., 1930

Seham, M., and Seham, G., "The Relation between Malnutrition and Nervousness," *American Journal of Diseases of Children,* XXXVII, January, 1929, pp. 1-38

Teachers' Problems with Exceptional Children—VI (Children of Low Vitality), United States Office of Education, Pamphlet No. 56, Government Printing Office, Washington, D. C., 1934

(F) *General References*

Allen, F. H., and Pearson, G. H. J., "The Emotional Problems of the Physically Handicapped Child," *British Journal of Medical Psychology,* VIII, 1928, pp. 212-235

Bentley, J. E., *Problem Children*, W. W. Norton & Company, New York, 1936

Endres, J. J., *The Education and Care of Physically Handicapped Children*, University of the State of New York, Bulletin No. 993, Albany, N. Y., 1932

Phair, J. T., and others, *Health—A Handbook for Teachers*, Ryerson Press, Toronto, 1938

The Journal of Exceptional Children, published monthly, October to May, by Harley Z. Woodene, East Lansing, Michigan

What Every Teacher Should Know about the Physical Condition of Her Pupils, United States Office of Education, Pamphlet No. 68, Government Printing Office, Washington, D. C., 1936

CHAPTER VIII

THE HOME AND THE COMMUNITY

I. PERSONALITY AND EARLY ENVIRONMENTAL INFLUENCES

From illustrative cases in the previous discussion we have seen that the mental-hygiene approach to children almost always involves a consideration of what is happening to the child outside school. It has been said again and again, and it will bear frequent repetition, that the pupil in school is also the child who lives at home. He eats, sleeps, works, and plays at home or in the neighborhood of his home about five sixths of his time. Only one sixth of his time is spent at school, even during the school term. It is almost impossible, therefore, to expect a child who is exposed to bad environmental influences away from school to develop a wholesome, robust personality simply through the efforts of a well-conducted educational program. The wonder is that occasionally this seems to occur.

The diagnostic approach must take into account the home and community. Many books have been written about them; this chapter sketches the main points of discussion.

II. THE FAMILY

Home and community as factors in the growth of personality are, in some ways, paradoxical to the development of the child's individuality. As he grows, he acquires ways of doing things, ways of behavior, that are peculiar to him, so that by the time he has approached the adult stage, he may be recognized as readily by his personality as by his name or face. This difference in personality, these peculiarities of behavior, taken together, represent his individuality. Curiously, however, as the child becomes more and more *himself,* he becomes more and more a part of the group of people who have contributed to his psychological development. Anyone who has observed an infant learning to recognize himself as one of a family has observed this social chemistry at work. At eight or nine years of age the child is not only himself, he is also whatever his father and mother are; anything that reflects on them, either of approval or disdain, reflects on him.

Nationality. In America children from families of foreign nationality were at one time frequently the butt of ridicule. "Blacky," "bohunk," "wop," these were examples of the names applied in ridicule to immigrants whose children attended school to learn the American way. In schools located in communities of foreign people, the fact of their alien nationality had usually no deleterious effect on the personalities of the children, but when American Anglo-Saxons outnumbered the Europeans, the latter were frequently alienated by the majority. Tricks, pranks, and even cruelty often sent the newly immigrated child home sobbing or infuriated to his parents.

The results of the treatment on the strange child were various. In many instances the children saw their parents' language and customs as the cause of their embarrassment and, to save themselves, broke from parental control. In such cases it sometimes occurred that the children, to attract the attention of their Anglo-Saxon "betters," to revenge themselves on the society that had caused them pain, or simply to make places for themselves in an opposing world, adopted forms of bravado that led many finally into antisocial conduct. Others were driven sullenly into communities where the national customs persisted, little affected by the surrounding Americanism.

It is not intended to suggest that these results occurred in a large proportion of cases; the American assimilation of the European has been one of the social phenomena of this century. But even yet the attitude of the American Anglo-Saxon toward people of foreign nationality is not one of wholehearted acceptance. Questionnaires still indicate a decided preference toward Anglo-Saxon, Celtic, and Scandinavian stock.

In the early days of immigration, the teacher was not always helpful in tempering children's attitudes toward the strangers. Often his point of view was little better than that of his pupils. It was another example of the obverse welcome that we accorded the immigrant whom we had invited to share in the good things the continent afforded—not only to share in them, but to assist us in exploiting the material and spiritual resources of a land comparatively free from the stultifying traditions of ten thousand years of living.

It is still pertinent, therefore, to suggest ways in which the teacher may deal with the problem of nationality.

His attitude should no doubt be that a child born of foreign parents is more than likely to have a contribution to make to the activities of the classroom and the work of the children who constitute it. If he is made to feel that he has something to give, and if he receives recognition for his offering, he will acquire solid security in his own mind. Further, his point of view toward his adopted country may be turned from the frequently observed "What can I get?" to the more valuable "What can I give?" Particularly in the activities of social studies and language the classroom contribution of the foreign child may enrich the child's own personality and affect valuably the points of view of the other children.

In one rural schoolroom the study of central Europe was carefully painted by the teacher's use of the peasant costumes that one of the pupils was able to bring from home. The result was not only a stimulus to the study of central Europe, but the creation of a new attitude toward the foreign pupil in the school and, finally, a development in one child's interest that led him to excel in women's dress designing as a vocation. Similar instances could be multiplied in which the teacher effectively used the contributions of foreign children to enrich the education of all the children in the school, and particularly to aid the foreign child to find security and a wholesome mutual attitude toward surroundings that would become increasingly familiar and benign.

Culture. It has been suggested that strangeness, lack of conformity, may provoke in children a tendency to aggressive behavior in the form of ridicule, mockery, teasing, or even bullying, designed to warp the nonconformist into the mold. The attitude of children toward various nationalities is directed, not so much because of possible biological differences between them and the strange one, but because of customs and forms of behavior different from their own.

Similarly, in American society itself appear groups of people with forms of speech, behavior, beliefs, which do not accord with those of the majority; and children born into these groups, if they must make their way in the public schools, may have a hard road to follow.

Thus, a boy whose father was a minister in a primitively emotional evangelical church usually found himself on the school grounds tagged with the nickname "Preacher" and followed by jeers of "Amen" and "Hallelujah." Sneers and jeers developed in him feelings of inferiority and diffidence that were likely to distort his personality. He avoided other school children, took the back-alley route home from school, or crossed the street to keep out of the way of those who might have been his playmates. Fortunately, before avoidance reactions and feelings of social insecurity had become definitely crystallized in his personality, the principal of the school became aware of the situation, found superior intelligence in the boy, and by public recognition of the boy's ability, gave him a place in his own esteem and that of the other children that quickly alleviated an undesirable effect.

In similar situations, the general procedure to be followed is one that objectifies the attitude of the child and his playmates toward the offending family customs. National peculiarities of speech may be a subject of class study; religious ceremonies may be compared with those common to the nation; tolerance itself may properly be worth examination.

Cultural level, in its broader sense, is a factor that must be regarded with concern in the diagnosis of personality problems. The older child, observing the difference in manner of dress, mode of speech, and deportment between his "uncultured" parents and the world that he meets at school, may be embarrassed in following the precept to honor his father and his mother. The resulting emotional conflict may be sufficiently serious to continue its detrimental influence throughout the individual's lifetime. One young lady, as the direct result of such influences, transferred her filial embarrassment into an aversion toward motherhood, and so clouded an otherwise lively and generous life. The process is so real and so frequently observed that at one time fiction written for boys and girls seldom omitted the character who was disgracefully ashamed of his parents and who was scorned by the reader accordingly.

In the development of this attitude in children, the school is not entirely blameless. Many people have wondered whether the school's emphasis on standards of speech, on knowledge as an attribute of success, on academic abilities as the insignia of culture is not representative of a pretty thin philosophy of education. Modern education values such things for what they are—tools which may help the child fashion his life; and as the usefulness of a tool grows in the hand that wields it, so do the academic tools become enhanced in value as the child employs them to assist him in understanding the society in which he lives and co-operating in its pursuits. In modern curriculums "the home" is the basis of study, and as children understand the place of the home, of *their* home, in social living, such cultural artifacts as speech, dress, and mannerisms acquire in the child's mind secondary importance.

At the same time, by the use of such curriculums intelligently applied, the school may offer the greatest assistance in improving the quality of home life and homemaking in a community.

Socio-economic Status. Wealth, as such, has little to do with the quality of home life, but the environment by which poverty may be surrounded and the qualities of mind that produce poverty are important factors in the disintegration of the home and the production of personality maladjustment.

The following figures, taken from a report of a survey in Boston of juvenile delinquency, represent the relationship of the mental condition of children to home and community environment: [1]

Illiteracy of parents 29%
Social welfare attendance 88%
Proportion of mothers working 40%
Proportion of wholesome homes 13%
Proportion of "favorable" neighborhoods 3%
Separation or divorce of parents 20%
Quarreling and wrangling parents 33%
Lax or unreasonable discipline 70%
Broken or poorly supervised homes 90%
Family delinquency 87%
Unhealthy mental conditions in family 86%

The unwholesome mental condition of the boys who had been arrested may be indicated by the following facts in addition to events that determined arrest and court appearance:

Retarded in school 85%
Left school to work 55%
Misspent leisure time 90%
Unassociated with organized recreational groups 75%
Previous misbehavior 95%
Truants 66%
Average age of first court appearance .... 9.7 years
Average number of arrests 2.3
Obvious emotional difficulties 80%

[1] Glueck, S. S., and Glueck, E., *One Thousand Juvenile Delinquents*, Harvard University Press, Cambridge, Mass., 1934. Reprinted by permission of the President and Fellows of Harvard College.

The relationship between these two sets of figures is too close to be coincidence. If conditions in the home and community are immediate causes of habitual delinquency and other indications of an unhealthy mental life, changes in the environment are indicated as remedial measures. Teachers, however, with heavy classroom duties, no matter how willing they may be, have little time or energy to devote to social welfare outside school. Probably the most that they can do to affect directly the conditions of the home is to co-operate as closely as possible with the various social agencies interested in such problems.

In spite of the fact that the influence of the teacher and the school on home conditions and on parents is an indirect one, the influence on the children themselves is direct and may be of inestimable value. In general the attitude of the teacher who would be successful in counteracting the influence of unwholesome behavior already engendered may be illustrated by the point of view of a rural supervisor who appointed a teacher to a village school with this comment: "I shall judge the success of your work, not by a battery of standard tests, nor by reading your lesson plans, but by the length of time it takes you to get those young fellows out of the pool hall and into some kind of creative leisure activity." Interest in useful creative activity may be readily developed in the schoolroom. Procedures for such development follow, in large measure, the recommendations that have been recorded previously in these pages.

Family Attitudes. From what has been said of the influence of nationality, culture, and socio-economic status, it is clear that all these affect the attitudes of the different members of the family toward one another, toward their neighborhood, and toward society as a whole. One has only to compare the different ways in which parents "train and discipline" their children to see how these factors affect the parents' attitudes toward their children. When a family, for instance, has long been living in crowded, cramped quarters, with scant financial security, it is easy to understand that, regardless of other factors, an emotional tension pervades the home. The attitudes of the parents and the older members of the family become emotionally toned and usually quite negativistic. The children "get on their nerves." Father and mother may shout, nag, and scold the children on the slightest provocation. Often severe corporal punishments alternate with periods of parental self-pity, during which the parents may be oversympathetic or lax in their dealings with the children. The consequent inconsistent discipline is thus emotional, rather than logical or rational.

In such an atmosphere bitter and aggressive family attitudes are easily developed. The parents are against the government, against the "relief racket," against society, and against the school. Unfortunately, it often seems as if they were also against the child. Psychiatrists have become increasingly interested in this question of parental rejection of the child. Symonds has recently studied the differences in personality development between children who were accepted and loved by their parents and children who were rejected: [2]

"This study brings out more clearly than previous studies the importance of parents' attitudes toward the children in the personality development of the child. The child who is

[2] Symonds, P. M., "A Study of Parental Acceptance and Rejection," *American Journal of Orthopsychiatry*, VIII: 4:679, October, 1938. (See page 686.)

wanted by his parents and grows up in a home atmosphere that is characterized by understanding and affection, loving care and protection, has every chance to develop into a well-balanced, emotionally stable adult. The child who is neglected or brutally treated by either parent, or even the child who is rejected in more subtle ways—by criticism, hostility, submerged under a cloak of insincere care and affection—is destined on the average to show strong aggressive traits, to be hostile and antagonistic toward those with whom he must have dealings, and to develop tendencies which may lead to delinquency."

In discussing Symonds's comment, Dr. H. W. Newell [3] described the apparently paradoxical behavior seen in these rejected children:

"They show a pathetic desire to be liked, while at the same time their behavior seems calculated to insure their being disliked. One possible picture of the mechanisms involved would describe these children as behaving according to the formula: 'My mother doesn't love me because I am bad. If I were good she would love me.' But with an intuitive sense of what the outcome would be, they do not dare take the risk of being good. They might fail and thus lose the benefit of a projection that serves to protect their ego. This formula helps to explain why the author found paranoid trends so frequently among rejected children."

The teacher's task under circumstances of family discord, either between the parents or between parents and child, is a problem that requires real tact if he attempts a direct appeal to the parents. The unmarried or childless teacher is in a particularly vulnerable position in giving parents advice about home discipline. A father of six children is likely to resent counsel from a childless

[3] *Ibid.*, page 688.

instructor. The least, and sometimes the most, that the teacher can do is to recognize the cause of the child's trouble and counteract it by objective treatment of the misconduct that has occurred. Too frequently teachers apply to the child already rejected by the parents a harsh form of treatment that aggravates the child's feeling of persecution and the consequent recessive or aggressive behavior. The teacher should realize that a sullen recessiveness or a bold antipathy in children in school seldom represents attitudes toward the teacher himself, but more often toward all authority.

Young teachers especially are likely to be greatly concerned by an apparent personal reaction on the part of the child. They resent it, and turn upon the pupil with a parallel quality of emotion. Perhaps the first lesson that the teacher should learn is that personalities of children are effects of powerful causes over which the children have had as little control as over the force of gravity.

To counteract the effect of parental rejection, teachers must first recognize it in their diagnosis, then apply countervailing measures. The chief of these is sympathetic interest in wholesome activities which the child seems to enjoy.

III. THE NEIGHBORHOOD AND THE COMMUNITY

Slums and Areas of Deterioration. Almost every city has its good and bad areas, whether the criterion for judging this goodness is wealth, excellence of buildings, living conditions, disease rates, death rates, crime rates, or the incidence of mental illness. As the city grows, the better-class residential areas get farther and farther from the center. In the older and more central areas, meanwhile, living conditions deteriorate. Tenements spring up. Old residences are converted first into rooming houses and then into flats. The final stage of deterioration is the slums, with all the overcrowding and unhealthy conditions which that term implies.

If we were to use pins to indicate on a map of any large city the residence of all delinquents appearing before the juvenile court during, say, the last two years, we would discover that these pins were clustered for the most part in certain areas. On closer observation we would probably be able to identify these areas as the slum, industrial, and business sections of the city.[4] Only an occasional pin would be placed in the better residential districts. The high incidence of delinquency in the slum areas demands some explanation. From the map, it looks almost as if delinquency were contagious and that it ran through children in the fashion of an epidemic. It is not reasonable to believe that the children of these districts have much lower I.Q.'s on the average than the children of the better-class districts, or that their delinquency represents, say, compensation for failure at school.[5] There must be social and cultural factors at work which are more or less common to the whole group. An understanding of the delinquent behavior in most cases can be obtained by reference to the diagrammatic scheme of needs and requirements outlined in Chapter II.[6] We find that in most of these delinquent children several of the basic needs, such as food, clothing, adequate protection, love, responsibility, recognition, are almost entirely

[4] Shaw, C. R., and McKay, H. D., *Social Factors in Juvenile Delinquency,* National Commission on Law Observance and Enforcement, No. 13, Report on Causes of Crime, Vol. II, Washington, D. C., 1931.

[5] Actually, surveys have revealed slight differences in the average I.Q. of children in slum areas as compared with children in good districts. This alone, however, will not explain the difference in delinquency rates.

[6] See page 23.

unsatisfied. Equally important is the high frequency in these areas of disorganized homes; so that not only is there a lack of high moral standards but there often is an absence of significant loyalties. Loyalty to parents or to other adults is not sufficiently powerful or meaningful to counteract the influence of delinquent playmates. Sometimes this latter influence grows into the more menacing pressure of gang loyalties. And sometimes, also, the parents and other adults in the home, either directly or indirectly, encourage delinquent behavior by their own attitude to the law.

It is interesting to compare these findings with a recent investigation into the geographic distribution of mental disorders. Faris and Dunham [7] studied the incidence of mental disorders in the different socio-economic areas of Chicago, Illinois, and Providence, Rhode Island. They found that the rates of mental disease ranged from a low of 110 cases per 100,000 of the adult population in the high-class residential area, to a high of 1757 in the central business districts and slum areas. There was a progressive lowering as the distance from the center of the city increased, with the exception of certain well-known deteriorated regions near the outskirts. In discussing the possible explanation for this distribution, the authors suggest that the nature of the social life and living conditions in certain areas of the city in some way contributes to the high rates of mental disorder. Inadequate social contacts in disorganized sections may produce a sense of isolation in the individual and place him in the role of an outcast. This undoubtedly would have a deleterious effect on the developing personality. Individuals living in com-

---

[7] Faris, R. E. L., and Dunham, H. W., *Mental Disorders in Urban Areas*, The University of Chicago Press, Chicago, Illinois, 1939.

munities not populated primarily by people of their own nationality or race were more liable to certain forms of mental disorder than when they were living among their own people.

We have indicated that delinquency and mental disease are not the only difficulties apparently related, in part, to socio-economic areas in the city. Investigation of children's behavior problems occurring in the schools of large cities show that these, too, occur more frequently in deteriorated and disorganized areas. The implication for the schools and, particularly, for teachers is obvious. Education must relate itself to the needs of the community. The teachers must become aware of the significance of social and economic pressures which exist in the area surrounding their own school. They must be prepared not only to understand the forces at work, but to do everything in their power to overcome the detrimental influences of these forces on the developing personality of the child.

Utilizing the Constructive Facilities. Most cities have a social-service exchange whereby the case work of the different social agencies in the city is co-ordinated. This exchange, or co-ordinating council, may serve a city, a county, or occasionally even a larger area. Co-operating in this exchange service are found most of the important agencies in the city dealing with social work and child welfare. When a teacher or a principal encounters a problem in a school which he feels is related to socio-economic factors in the home or community, he can often obtain a great deal of help through an appeal to one or another of these agencies. In order to determine what agencies, if any, are already active in the family, he should call the Social Service Exchange (or Co-ordinating Council, as the case may be). If the teacher finds that a social-welfare or child-welfare agency already knows the family, it is a comparatively simple matter to call the particular agency in order to obtain information. It must be remembered that much of the information collected in case work is highly confidential; and the agency may well be reluctant to discuss this information freely unless it is sure of the integrity of the person who makes the inquiry. Unfortunately, it is the experience of most social agencies that information passed out too readily may be used unwisely. The teacher or principal must be prepared, therefore, to impress the agency active in the particular case with his honesty of purpose and with his ability to use to good advantage the information divulged. In any event, a personal interview with the social worker who knows the family will very rarely be refused, and this can be most helpful in understanding the child.

Most social workers realize that the teacher is in rather a unique position to help the child and, indirectly, the whole family. Often when no social agency is active, the teacher can be instrumental in getting some action started. In this connection, the teacher can often pave the way so that the family are prepared to receive help. Many times all that is needed is an interpretation to the parents of the kind of help and service that is available.

The number and types of social-welfare agencies vary from city to city. Most large centers nowadays have special courts for juvenile offenders. These juvenile courts usually operate on the general principle that delinquency is an indication of social and personal maladjustment. The hopelessness and complete ineffectiveness of arrest and punishment as measures directed towards crime prevention are now generally recognized. Attached to most of these juvenile courts are psychiatric and psychological services. In many centers Big Brother and Big Sister associations are active organizations which endeavor to re-establish children in wholesome social and recreational activities and, where possible, to correct the environmental factors at fault. Often the help of these organizations can be obtained directly without having the child go through the juvenile court. Other typical organizations interested in children's problems include children's protective societies (such as the Children's Aid), family relief and rehabilitation agencies, the various health clinics and agencies, psychiatric and psychological clinics, and recreational organizations of all types.

When for any reason the teacher or principal is not in a position to use the community social agencies, there is still a great deal that he can do by himself. In almost every case his attack on the problem begins with an interview or a visit with the parents. With foreign-born parents often all that is necessary is an explanation and interpretation of the customs and opportunities of the New World.

Occasionally the teacher can help the child to make better use of his spare time out of school. Where idleness and bad companions have contributed to problem behavior, the child can be introduced to the local Boy Scout or Girl Guide organization. If the teacher takes the trouble to look up the scout leader and explain in some detail the problem, as he sees it, a much greater co-operation can usually be obtained, which will, in turn, be of great benefit to the child. Exactly the same thing holds for the local Y.M.C.A. and the Y.W.C.A. and certain church organizations. In many centers groups in handicraft work, hobbies, and other special activities have been organized in connection with the Y.M.C.A. and the Y.W.C.A. It will usually be found that the local agencies, such as the Big Brother and Big Sister, are utilizing these facilities to the full, and that children with special problems will be made very welcome.

To teachers in rural areas most of what has been said above may sound remote and abstract. Few rural communities have a sufficiently complex social organization to warrant the establishment of such institutions as the Y.M.C.A.'s, or even church clubs and Boy Scouts. In such a situation the teacher may wonder what constructive facilities are available, if any. The further from an urban center that a rural community is situated, the more need will there be for the teacher to rely on the constructive facilities at hand in his own school and school district. If there is no boys' club, for example, why could not one be organized from the school group? If the teacher feels he is not able to do this, perhaps he can rally the interest and active assistance of someone else— the local minister, an interested young farmer, or some such person. The particular talent available in the community must determine to a degree the nature of the groups organized. Often the only reason no group activities are available in country churches is the fact that no one has had the interest or enthusiasm to organize them. The teacher can do much to stimulate activity of this kind, even in remote areas.

Rural communities are seldom lacking in "social" life, in the ordinary sense of the term. It should require no unusual amount of genius to convert some of these "socials" into regular events of really constructive value.

There is no limit to the scope here. Amateur dramatics, cooking classes, sports, gym classes, a Boy Scout troop—

all these may develop in a natural way from activities already partially organized in the district. Surely the challenge which this presents is enough to counterbalance any apparent advantage of the urban center with all its ready-made "facilities."

IV. HOME-AND-SCHOOL ORGANIZATIONS [8]

We have seen that the school is a social agency profoundly affected by the point of view, the traditions, and the background of the community. The two are inseparable. No teacher can hope to make important changes in the policy of his school without having the backing of the public of his district. Policies regarding discipline, extracurricular activities, newer methods of teaching, and newer methods of organization will not succeed without a reasonable measure of community understanding and support. The home-and-school association affords an opportunity for the teacher to win such support. It also affords an excellent medium through which fine parent-teacher co-operation and mutual understanding can be fostered.

Many home-and-school clubs, however, become sidetracked with projects and goals of a less essential type. Some clubs have come to grief because they have attempted to dictate policy and interfere with the administration of the school. This is not the purpose of such clubs. Discussions may, and often should, affect the policy of the principal or the school board; but the final responsibility rests with the regularly elected and appointed authorities. Similarly, many clubs become involved in social activities, whist drives, dances, concerts,

[8] These organizations are called by various names: Parent-Teacher Association; Home and School Club; Home and School Association, etc.

and such. Usually there are other organizations supplying the social needs of the community, without involving the school staff or premises. While there is no objection to the occasional social evening, the whole energy of the club should not be directed in this way. The same criticisms can be directed to those clubs whose chief goal seems to be the raising of funds, even though these funds are to be devoted to very worth-while needs. The purchase of playground equipment, for example, is the responsibility of the school authorities. The club can, however, become an important agency in developing public opinion on the matter, so that the authorities will feel justified in making such purchases.

What, then, *should* a home-and-school club be? It should exist in order that teachers and parents may *study together* problems concerning the education of children. Primarily, therefore, it should be a study club. It should provide an ideal setting and opportunity for the teachers to lend educational leadership to the community. It should make possible in practice that co-operation between home and school which we have discussed at length in this chapter. While the teachers, as educational experts, should provide the leadership, the parents should assume the responsibility for the executive and administrative work of the club and the arrangement of programs.

Generally speaking, it is far more desirable to arrange a topic for study and discussion than to have an important speaker come to address the club. Parents become more actively interested when they begin to talk and express their own ideas. A few suitable topics for discussion are suggested at the end of this chapter, together with useful literature.

The problem of *when* to organize a home-and-school club needs some consideration. Undoubtedly, the community should be "ready" for it; and this usually means that interested teachers and laymen must prepare the ground for it by arousing interest in other community clubs and organizations. Very little progress can be made if the principal and teachers are not solidly behind the project and sympathetic with its aims. Valuable assistance can often be obtained in planning such a club from the state or provincial home-and-school organization, when such exists.

V. SOME CONCLUSIONS

In this chapter we have tried to emphasize the mental-hygiene significance of influences lying outside the school —the family, the home, and the neighborhood. As teachers striving to understand children in school, we have seen that it is impossible to avoid paying some attention to these influences. In the school child are focused most of the environmental forces of the community. If we wish to influence the child's developing character and personality in positive directions, we must not only understand and appreciate these environmental forces, but we must be prepared to co-operate with others in the community (parents in particular). To a certain degree we must be prepared to provide leadership in the belief that progress in mental hygiene and education can best be achieved through informed and enlightened public opinion.

APPENDIX A

Suggested Topics for Discussion at Home-and-School Clubs

I. *Meaning and purpose of education*
1. What Is the Purpose of the School?
2. The Functions of Partnership
3. The Good Teacher
4. The Good Parent
5. The School as a Democratic Institution
6. The School as a Builder of Personality
7. What Are the End Products of Education?

II. *The Child*
1. Individual Differences in Children
2. How the Bright Child Can Be Helped to Realize His Possibilities
3. Safeguarding the Personality of Dull Children
4. The Mental Health Needs of Children
5. Special Education for Exceptional Children (Dull, Bright, Deaf, Blind, Crippled, etc.)
6. Emotional Development of Children
7. Understanding Children's Problems
8. What Is the "Problem Child"?

III. *Methods of Teaching and Organization in Schools*
1. Why We Teach by the Project Method
2. What Is an Activity Program?
3. Modern Ways of Teaching Reading
4. Modern Methods in Geography
5. The Value of Play in Child Development
6. The Purpose of Athletics in a School Program
7. The Place of Dramatics and Literary Societies in School Programs
8. The Place of Libraries in Education

APPENDIX B

I. Pamphlets

Great help in preparing discussions on such topics as are listed in Appendix A can be obtained from pamphlets which are available for a few cents from several national organizations. Interested teachers and parents should write for a complete catalogue.

National Committee for Mental Hygiene, 50 West 50 Street, New York, N. Y.

National Committee for Mental Hygiene (Canada), 111 St. George Street, Toronto, Ontario

Child Study Association of America, Inc., 221 West 57 Street, New York, N. Y.

United States Department of Labor (Children's Bureau), Washington, D. C.

American Association for Adult Education, Inc., 60 East 42 Street, New York, N. Y.

Metropolitan Life Insurance Company, Ottawa, Canada, and New York, N. Y.

Canadian Welfare Council, Council House, Ottawa, Canada

State and Provincial Departments of Mental Hygiene

II. Magazines

Parents' Magazine, 4600 Diversey Street, Chicago, Illinois

Child Study, Child Study Association

Understanding the Child, National Committee for Mental Hygiene (United States and Canada)

Journal of Exceptional Children, Butler, Indiana

III. Books

In addition to the books referred to in the lists given from time to time throughout this book, the following will be found of special use in study groups and in consultation work with parents:

Anderson, H. H., *Children in the Family*, D. Appleton-Century Company, Inc., New York; Ryerson Press, Toronto, 1937

Brill, A. C., and Youtz, M., *Your Child and His Parents*, D. Appleton-Century Company, Inc., New York, 1932

Faegre, Marion L., and Anderson, John E., *Child Care and Training* (Fourth Edition, Revised), University of Minnesota, Minneapolis, Minn., 1937

Fletcher, B. A., *Child Psychology for Parents*, Ryerson Press, Toronto, 1938

Witty, P. A., and Skinner, C. E. (Editors), *Mental Hygiene in Modern Education*, Farrar & Rinehart, Inc., New York, 1939

The resources of local libraries should be combed. Often help may be obtained from the Department of Child Psychology in the local state or provincial university.

CHAPTER IX

THE SCHOOL; PROBLEMS OF ORGANIZATION AND ADMINISTRATION

I. MENTAL HYGIENE AND PEDAGOGY

In Chapter II the development of personality was discussed in terms of the child's fundamental needs and social requirements. The school of the present day frankly adopts the point of view that in all phases of its administration and program those needs and requirements must be met to the fullest possible extent. Educational planning centers around the problems of healthful development. It is definitely not our purpose, however, to deal with the more formal aspects of educational organization. These are the concern of the expert in pedagogy and administration. Nevertheless, assuming that all aspects of education—curriculum, records, discipline, examinations, and the like—have significance for the healthy development of the child, then all these come within our field of interest, at least to some extent. At this point, therefore, we may conveniently examine various aspects and problems of school organization and administration, considering briefly their bearing upon the mental health of the pupils at all times.

II. THE CURRICULUM

There was a time when school curriculums were relatively inflexible. They consisted of an orderly sequence of facts and skills to be taught. Individual differences among pupils were not considered to any very great extent, save that a rigid system of uniform standards made it necessary for some children to work harder or for longer periods of time, in order to secure the periodic promotion from one grade to another. The needs of all children were deemed to be identical, and these were defined almost exclusively in terms of things to be learned.

In contrast with all this, the present-day courses of studies endeavor to make provision for individual differences, to anticipate at all times the child's social needs, and to foster spontaneity of effort that is conducive to personal satisfaction and social benefit. We quote from recently published statements of program for the elementary schools:

"The curriculum is to be thought of in terms of activity and experience, rather than of knowledge to be acquired and facts to be stored." [1]

"The school must follow the method of nature, stimulating the child, through his own interests, into activities and guiding him into experiences useful for the satisfaction and development of *his* needs." [2]

"Instruction should be fitted to the needs of the individual. Pupils differ in native intellectual capacity and in physical nature. . . . They differ in background, outlook and ambition." [3]

These aims are reflected in the following principles which underlie the planning of modern curriculums:

(*a*) *The curriculum should be suited to the capacity of the pupil.* This principle shows itself in more adequate provision for brighter pupils and for those not quite so

[1] *The Primary School,* Report of the Consultative Committee of the Board of Education, Great Britain, 1931.
[2] *Programme of Studies for Grades I to VI,* Ontario, 1937.
[3] *Programme of Studies for the Elementary Schools of British Columbia,* Bulletin I, 1936.

well equipped mentally, and in more careful attention to the relationship between difficulty of subject matter and the mental age of the learner. The older practice of trying to demand one standard for all has frankly been discarded. Many applications of this principle are given in chapters V and VI.

(*b*) *The curriculum should be in line with the needs of the pupils.* All materials and curricular content are now scrutinized in relation to the present and future needs of the pupils. Only in this way can experiences in the classroom be closely integrated with the realities of the child's life and outlook. The needs are related to his general capacity and special abilities, his physique and social maturity, and the community in which he lives.

(*c*) *The curriculum should provide for social and emotional development of the child, as well as for his intellectual development.* Not only is there more careful selection of the basic intellectual content of the program, but also a better planning of all activities, so that worthwhile appreciations, attitudes, and interests are cultivated. Meaning takes on a more intimate role than heretofore. It represents personal progress, understanding, satisfaction, participation. It involves creation, contribution to the social life of the group, assumption of responsibility, development of self-knowledge, and self-confidence in one's abilities. Every aspect of factual learning bears directly upon the child's greater understanding of the problems of social living and his opportunities for an enriched and more significant experience.

(*d*) *The curriculum must be of such a nature that it develops initiative in children and encourages spontaneity.* Learning is an active process. Its direction may be largely supervised (for example, by the teacher), or it may be controlled by the interests and plans of the learner. Self-direction in learning has to be achieved. It, too, involves a learning process. Increasingly, therefore, as the child develops he must be given an opportunity to exercise some direction of his own. He needs practice in planning, in raising questions, in discussing problems, in spontaneous inquiry, in research. He does not find everything in his program cut and dried; *flexibility* is becoming more and more the keynote—flexibility to the degree warranted by the child's demonstrated ability to be spontaneous, yet at the same time to contribute to the experience of his fellows. Only in so far as this spontaneity is cultivated can he achieve real security in his outlook—a principle that is fundamental to the enterprise and activity programs so characteristic of the modern school.

(*e*) *The curriculum must provide for its own integration through use.* The principle of integration is applied so as to ensure meaningful relationships among all aspects of the program. In practice, this means that the subject matter is constantly involved in daily use, in enterprises that draw upon the facts and skills acquired and apply them to concrete everyday tasks and projects.

III. EXTRACLASSROOM ACTIVITIES

The spirit of modern education, with its emphasis on fostering the development of healthy, effective personalities, has led to a breakdown of the old distinction between academic schoolwork and "afterschool" activities as represented by athletics, dramatics, debates, and other projects which have not always been listed as a definite part of the course of studies. In addition to those mentioned above, they include such endeavors as the literary society, the glee club, the school orchestra, the school paper, the science club, and many others. These activities may be as carefully planned as the work in history, literature, and mathematics. Indeed, in the truly progressive school the academic subjects and the so-called extracurricular or extraclassroom activities are integrated so as to act in a unified way to promote healthy development and growth. In many schools such activities are an organized part of the daily work during school hours. If this part of the program is to be adequately carried out, the teachers must be prepared to give more than usual thought to the individual needs and interests of the children. Here individuality should get its finest co-operation and encouragement, since each child will be following interests of his own and contributing to the group according to his own ability.

Today the schools are not content to lose interest in the child as soon as he leaves the school for home. More and more interest is being taken by educationists in what may be really described as extramural activities. No longer is the school a place where the child's life stands in marked contrast with his life elsewhere. It is true that outside school hours the expression and direction exercised by the teacher is more indirect. But if the school accepts its responsibility in the matter of child training, it must be interested in the form of the child's experience after the school gates are closed. For this reason every teacher should become acquainted with the general pattern of his pupils' interests and activities at home, in their social groups beyond the school. Where this seems to be inadequate, he can do much during school hours to supplement each child's repertoire of interests and useful accomplishments. He can often sense the most vital contribution that the school can make to the child by appraising the lines along which he proceeds when school influence is relaxed. Parent-teacher co-operation has a sound basis only when the whole life of the child is taken into consideration, rather than just that part which traditionally was thought of as "schooling."

In some cases, despite the teacher's efforts in school, the child will still have a very inadequate extraschool program. Co-operation with the parents and with social organizations can then foster distinctly positive contributions along such lines as Y.M.C.A. activities, sports groups, church clubs, Scouts, Guides, summer camps, and so on. Where these are not readily available, the school itself can become a real community center; and, indeed, the school should always be ready to play its part as one of the co-operating community organizations, adapting its role after school hours in accordance with community needs. Hobby clubs, concerts, drama, arts and crafts, scientific meetings, musical societies, sports clubs, and so on readily suggest themselves as specific lines along which widespread interest can readily and profitably be aroused.

Hobbies. Recent literature contains a great deal of discussion concerning hobbies. There is little question about the fact that a healthy mental outlook demands plenty of absorbing and challenging activity, with enough variety to maintain interest, to stimulate all sides of one's nature, and to provide a ready balance between individual and group participation. In many vocations such variety and constant stimulation are not readily possible, although the more progressive industrial leaders are realizing their importance. Where one's vocational life is of necessity somewhat cramped, leisure-time activities must supply the deficiency; and education has an enormous responsibility in equipping the child for leisure. Curricular and extracurricular activities all contribute to this end.

Theoretically, there should be no need for hobbies as "compensations." Ideally, all aspects of our life should be closely co-ordinated, interrelated in a perfectly smooth and harmonious way, each aspect contributing positively to our total well-being. But unless we are on our guard, we are all in danger of becoming lopsided—too prone to work alone, or too prone to be completely lost unless working with a group; too dependent upon one set of associates, with restricted interests, or too spread-eagled and superficial in our social contacts; too absorbed in our narrow groove, or too diverse in our activities so that along no one line do we make anything like as significant a contribution as we are capable of doing. A well-balanced pattern of living is difficult to achieve, but it is most decidedly worth cultivating.

If thought of in this sense, hobbies do not represent mere correctives for a poorly balanced pattern of living. They take their place in the scheme of things representing our life. We need work and play; we need group activities and individual lines of interest; we need creative enterprises that are bound up with the well-being of ourselves, as well as those that essentially contribute to, and are undertaken for, the benefit of others. In all forms of endeavor we express our own peculiar gifts and recognize our weaknesses, so that through the medium of our whole personality we intimately relate the various aspects of our life and behavior. The more consistent the picture of variety displayed by our life, the more satisfying, smooth, and harmonious that life becomes. The more the hobby stands out in contrast to the rest of our existence, the more likelihood is there that it is a mere corrective for lack of balance somewhere in our way of living.

On the whole, the important thing is not the hobby as such. Whatever the form of the activity, it should give expression to the same principles of sound development that apply everywhere. In that case, distinctions between work and play, vocation and leisure, are hard to maintain and are not readily distinguishable in our own experience.

IV. GRADING AND PROMOTION

In any school system some form of grouping will be necessary, for reasons of economy and because of the benefits of social participation. There is greater recognition today, however, of the fact that the established—and comparatively recent—nature of our grading system tends to have certain artificial features that we are now trying to overcome. Thus, many schools still persist in grading on the basis of age, rather than of mental maturity; of reading accomplishment (as in Grade One and Grade Two), rather than of social needs and stimulating experience. There is obviously greater need for considering the child's social environment as a whole in relation to his educational requirements than is the case when grading standards are entirely determined by the amount of knowledge and skill thus far acquired in past experience.

From the standpoint of mental hygiene, the following principles emerge:

(*a*) Each child should obviously work with the group in which his development proceeds most effectively. The academic work involved is, of course, a basic consideration. Hence, matters of I.Q. and mental age, past training, future purpose, continuity of the subject matter, all enter into the picture. In addition, there are factors of social participation, creativeness, emotional understandings, and expressions.

(*b*) Other factors being equal, a child can work most successfully in any class when the average mental age of the pupils approximates his own.[4]

(*c*) The grading system should be flexible enough to reduce repetition of a year's work to a minimum. The mental-hygiene significance of "failure," particularly in the early school years, is obvious.

(*d*) Opportunities should exist for a certain amount of variety in grouping. This will ensure that the child experiences situations in which he will give leadership, others in which he will play a co-operative yet less major part. He will sometimes be working with a group to whom he makes a very significant contribution, because of his own personal culture and ability; at other times, with a group from whom he receives a great deal of stimulation that comes from a background of experience other than his own. In many instances this variety will come mainly within the society constituted by his own class or grade; but it need by no means be limited to this.

(*e*) The most comprehensive principle is that grading should be determined by the child's own response. If a new child is admitted to the school, he should be placed with the group that seems likely to be most fitting for his requirements on the basis of age, mental age, and such characteristics. This tentative placement should be watched critically and constructively. No hard and fast rules can be laid down. Consequently, the revision of any

[4] For a discussion of "mental age" and tests of intelligence, both group and individual, see page 96.

tentative grading will be largely determined by the behavior demonstrated by the child. If he is energetic, alert, obviously learning and progressing, contributing to the life of the group, profiting by his associations with them, he is in the right place. If he is bored or unduly puzzled, antagonistic or merely watchful and submissive, bombastic or excessively timid, some change is necessary. Grade placement is an art.

V. QUESTIONS AND EXAMINATIONS

Pedagogical literature has much to say about the art of interrogation. With this aspect of questioning we are not here concerned. Rather, our considerations refer to the development of a healthy questioning attitude, an attitude that represents an objective search for truth on the one hand, and a genuine interest in one's associates on the other. A few suggestions pertinent to this matter are given in what follows:

(*a*) Encourage the child to raise questions himself. He needs practice in setting his own problems and in formulating, under direction, his own projects.

(*b*) As far as possible, direct these problems and projects along lines that make possible the answering of many of his inquiries through his own efforts. Instead of telling him the answer immediately, direct his search, or search with him.

(*c*) Whenever a well-rounded-out line of inquiry nears completion, set the stage so that further problems arise. While the solution to these problems may not be undertaken immediately, it is well to leave room for a definite line of further inquiry. Even if many of these lines of inquiry are not pursued, they assist in fostering an open-mindedness so necessary for both the scientific attitude to the world and satisfactory social relationships. In addition, there is always the possibility of the question "How does this apply to problems in other settings?" However clearly a story of fact or a story of relationship is told, it should lead immediately to further inquiry. In this connection, it is interesting to note that the more recent and stimulating textbooks for pupils are characterized by this form of stimulation.

(*d*) Question *with* the child, more frequently than you question the child himself to see what he knows.

(*e*) Avoid dogmatic answers to his questions. Where questions of fact can be answered by you without detracting from the value of his enterprise in his own eyes, short-cut his inquiry. That is one of the main functions of teaching. But do not base your whole teaching procedure on telling him things that *you* know and *he* does not. A healthy teacher-pupil relationship can never be established on this basis. The pupil must have confidence in you and your answers; but he must also experience the joy of finding out things for himself, if he is to become a self-directing individual. Our best technique for stopping his inquiry along wasteful or less desirable lines is to tell him the answer concerned. But our best technique for stimulating further inquiry is to give him the joy of achievement. These two principles are the basis of our function in *directing* his inquiries. If we want him to appreciate the meaning and usefulness of a given fact, we must lead him to inquire into a problem where the solution will depend in part upon that fact. This is the meaning of *practice,* as opposed to "drill" by repeating the fact itself.

(*f*) There sometimes arise certain undesirable forms of questioning on the part of the child—questions which are asked for the sole purpose of getting attention, or which reflect an "inquisitive" interest in gossip. These forms obviously reflect inadequacies of social adjustment and development. The undesirable features of questioning are usually best handled by the child's social peers. In a thoroughly enterprising social group, they disappear because of the more satisfying experiences of purposeful activity.

With reference to questions designed to find out what a child knows—questions of the "examination" type— the chief points to raise, from the mental-hygiene point of view, are the following:

(*a*) Examinations are not harmful in themselves. Their weakness comes from the way in which they are conducted. All through life we have to meet examinations —whenever we drive a car, we are testing ourselves in many ways; the surgeon meets a real examination with every operation he performs; the boy who pitches ball is examining his skill with every throw; and so on. We must, therefore, train the child in examining himself, in being constantly alert to his own possibilities for improvement—in skill and in every branch of social relationships and human endeavor.

(*b*) The teacher should not set himself up as the only examiner of the child, or even as the most frequent or most important examiner. Another child, a classmate, a parent, or any other associate may temporarily be the examiner, particularly when the child himself is ready to be examined.

(*c*) Often a child will *ask* to be examined. Foster this, particularly when it is a real desire on his part to make an objective appraisal of what he has learned. Let him look upon the examination form of questioning not as a competitive strain, surrounded by an aura of fear, but as a necessary and enjoyable part of self-appraisal, from which his sense of progressive achievement may be healthfully fostered. Speed competitions should be avoided, save when the child is eager to test his own skill, without reference to that of others. The latter involves emotional strain and social antagonisms.

(*d*) Do not use the examination as a goal, but rather as a means of encouraging the child's understanding of his own progress, his lines of strength, his avenues of worth-while creativeness and social participation.

(*e*) In most educational settings the "recommendation" system is growing, so that we no longer depend entirely upon the external authority for setting examinations. External examinations undoubtedly have their place. For example, if a child wishes to get a job in a given industry, or to enter a given profession, he can readily be motivated to understand that the industry or profession must of necessity set certain standards and that he must meet the standards if he wishes to participate in these lines of endeavor. But the function of the recommendation system is to foster the tendency towards self-appraisal, towards looking upon our problem solving in daily work as a means of challenging our efforts and indicating our progress in achievement. To substitute a set of school examinations for those of the outside authority misses the point of this educational revision entirely.

(*f*) There should not be *fewer* examinations, but *more*. Every task should challenge us. But the motivation, the meaning behind the examination, is all-important. The transition from checking our progress by our own problem solving and projects, to checking our progress by answering the questions, performing tasks, and solving problems set by others, is an easy one in a well-ordered school. There need be no more emotional strain in examinations than in everyday life. In so far as there is, we as educators are weak in fulfilling our function; and emotional strain should at all times be watched, and corrected whenever possible by directing it into channels of expression that are personally worth-while and socially contributing.

(*g*) Avoid artificiality of the standards involved in examinations. Give the children plenty of practice in setting examinations for one another, as well as in writing them. Let the children take turnabout in questioning and answering one another, whenever possible.

(*h*) When the more formal examinations are used— for these, of course, have their place—remember that if the purpose of the examination is to explore the child's knowledge of fundamental facts, careful sampling of these facts must be taken into consideration. We cannot ask about them all. (The educational psychologist's emphasis on new-type examinations is pertinent here.) Give plenty of weight in your appraisal of the child's progress to what he can do with the facts as a basis—in construction, in conversation, in essay and applicative work, and so on. This is the real test of how well the facts are understood. Also, give a wide scope for observing his progress in everyday activities.

VI. RECORDS AND REPORTS

The Need for Records. In practically every provincial and state system of education on this continent the teacher is required to keep records of pupils in school registers or on record cards or forms. This is often regarded as a tedious task imposed by the authorities, having little meaning or permanent worth, unless the real purposes of record keeping are appreciated. We must, therefore, inquire at the outset as to why such records are kept.

Records are a means to an end. They provide data which the administrator finds of great value. The administrator, having no direct contact with individual children, yet responsible for framing and evaluating the school program as a whole, relies to a considerable extent upon records of attendance, retardation, achievement, physical defects, home conditions, and community needs. He must see to it that information is constantly being gathered that will enable him to make the necessary provision for special classes, remedial work in speech, medical inspection, and a host of other things. In his planning, he is helped considerably by being able to compare his school program and its outcome with those of other systems. Broad progress in education is thus dependent to a degree on the keeping of pertinent records.

To the classroom teacher, the principal, the school nurse, the physician, the psychologist, the visiting teacher —to all who are directly concerned with the welfare of the individual child—the records are of great value in the process of education itself. By keeping careful note of various aspects of children's progress, the basis is laid for transforming education from a mass-informing procedure to one of effectively directing each individual child and helping him to solve his own particular problems. Still further, the matter of recording is in itself a very significant factor in enriching the teacher's understanding of what to observe, how to describe each child's progress in ways that are pertinent to questions of development; and by this means, too, there is furnished a basis for discussing significant educational matters with parents.

Records. From the angle of administration, the following facts are usually recorded: name, age, sex, school, grade; age on entering school, schools attended, number of days in each grade, date of entering each grade, attendance, lateness; names and nationality of parents, occupation of father; physical and medical history; achievement ratings (or marks) in each major school subject.

Facts of this type are very useful in appraising the degree to which the system is functioning smoothly along the main lines indicated by the general administrative setting. They assist in judging the gross features of the educational needs of the community. With these aspects we are not primarily concerned here, important as they undoubtedly are.

When we come to the more intimate aspects of records, with which the teacher himself is mainly concerned, the records become more complicated, less stereotyped, and somewhat harder to define. For children in general, certain observations are recorded which indicate the degree to which satisfactory progress along all the major lines of development is being made. Where difficulty arises, a more complete, detailed, and diagnostic analysis is made of the individual and his particular problems. In this chapter we are mainly concerned with the former situation. Diagnostic recording has been treated in Chapter IV.

One consideration that cannot be lost sight of is economy of time in recording. Useless records are time-consuming and irksome. It would seem that, in addition to the basic facts recorded for administration purposes— some of which are cumulative in nature—the essential aspects of a cumulative record of each child's development are the following:

(1) *Intellectual development.* (a) Mental age and I.Q. should be determined by group tests for all children two or three times during the elementary-school period. This is most conveniently done at Grade One or Grade Two, at the fourth grade, and at the seventh-grade and eighth-grade levels.

(b) The teacher's appraisal of the general mental caliber of the child should be indicated. Where this differs from the result of the group test, the discrepancy should be noted. If possible, the teacher should also state his reason for his judgment concerning the discrepancy.

(c) An individual test should be administered by a competent examiner if the discrepancy is marked.

(d) Some indication of the grade or level of the school program which is being covered at the time should be given. If the child is achieving in his grade in accordance with his mental caliber, no further comment is necessary. If he is doing much better work than is expected, this should be noted. Special reference should be made to particularly absorbing interests, methods of systematic work, evidences of poorly balanced programs of work, such as the concentration on academic work at the expense of social activities, and so on. Information of this type may illuminate the discrepancy between appraised ability and observed accomplishment, and may assist in understanding the child's developing interests. In all cases where achievement and ability do not seem to harmonize, interpretive notes and complete information on the action taken should be recorded.

(e) Achievement in individual subjects need not be recorded unless it is out of line with what is known about the child, his abilities and capacities. Strong points and weak points, where these appear to indicate developing interests or aversions, should receive attention, and appropriate notations should be made.

(*f*) There is always a place for descriptive comment, in addition to the recordings under appropriate headings (above). Attitude toward work, consistency of effort and purposeful outlook, planning, systematic work habits, and use of time are typical points of importance to note, particularly when they suggest the need of further guidance.

(2) *Emotional and social development.* These aspects are perhaps best considered in the following section. Reports to parents and special reports will form part of the child's cumulative record, and unnecessary duplication and overlap will be avoided. However, in reporting to parents, the incidents and achievements in the school setting will not always be mentioned. They serve as the evidence for the conclusions regarding the child's development and should be filed with the school records.

Reports to Parents.[5] The teacher is responsible for the material reported to the parents, even though the form of the report is determined by the administrator. The reports offer a splendid avenue for parent-teacher cooperation, and should be regarded essentially in this light. As indicated above, they also form part of the cumulative record kept by the school.

These reports should reflect the educational philosophy of the school. If that philosophy is conceived in terms of social and healthy mental development, if it is concerned with what the pupils *are* and *are becoming,* as well as

[5] When a *special report* is required by the clinic or a social agency for purposes of diagnosis, the method outlined on page 109 will be satisfactory.

with what they know, it will reflect itself in the type of report given. A brief statement of aims is often, therefore, a worth-while preface on the front of every report card. But more significant is the form which the body of the report assumes.

We would suggest that progress be reported under certain general headings, such as "Intellectual," "Emotional," "Social." These headings need not appear on the report card, but can be kept in mind by the teacher in reporting. Concerning intellectual development, it seems advisable to avoid all reference to competitive standards. If parents tend to demand information as to how their children are doing relative to others in the class, a little attention to parent education through the medium of discussing the reports, in groups or with the particular parents concerned, will eventually take care of this factor. There is really no need to quote marks or class standing. Satisfactory work should be recorded; special interests and achievements will receive appropriate comment; weak spots may be mentioned, so that an interview with the parents may be arranged and a plan of action undertaken that will be helpful to the child. The school records will undoubtedly include diagnostic detail and factual evidence for all this. But parental misinterpretation of marks and class standing can best be avoided by some such means as suggested above, or even by having the parent visit the school to see what the child is doing and enjoying. Interpretative comments on the report, concerning possible causes of weakness, should be used with caution. They should be noted on the school records; but they are best left at that point until they can be talked over frankly with the parent. The same holds true for helpful or remedial measures.

Social and emotional aspects will give some difficulty until the teacher becomes efficient and effective in reporting along these lines. On the whole, the *positive* side should be stressed on the report card or form.[6] If the child in the primary grades, for example, is working and playing appropriately with his social group, if he seems to be alert, happy, busy, interested in his work and in his fellows, constructive in his efforts and social participation, emotionally in tune with the group, and, while friendly with all, finding special companionship with a suitable circle of friends, these facts should be mentioned. Similarly, if a child in the fourth grade is developing in the direction of team play, in organizing and participating in informal clubs or groups; if he is capable of assuming adequate responsibility, relative to his age; if he has a positive attitude toward his work, himself, and others; if he demonstrates a healthy interest in discussion; if he begins to show initiative and enterprise in his projects or hobbies; or if a child in the seventh or eighth grade has broadened his outlook so that his ambitions or inquiries concerning his next stages in training are taking legitimate and worth-while shape—then these and similarly positive observations should be stated. The teacher has an invaluable opportunity here of challenging himself and of directing the thinking of parents along constructive lines. School cumulative records may go beyond this, as before, and give suitable and detailed evidence in relation to development.

If the child's social and emotional progress is slightly below par, the techniques of the school are probably adequate to take care of this without reporting the matter

[6] Reference should be made to "Norms of Healthy Personality Development," page 11.

to the parents. When this is so, school records may note the fact; but there seems to be no purpose in running the risk of gross exaggeration by reporting to the parent a matter that the school can take care of adequately. For example, on entering school in the kindergarten or first grade, the child, because of the nature of his home background, early training, and the like, may find some difficulty in adjusting to group living in school. But in most cases the school is able to take care of such difficulties if the possibility of their existence is adequately realized. If, on the other hand, social and emotional progress are such that active co-operation with the home is necessary, a carefully framed statement inviting a discussion of the child's progress—without undue comment—is usually sufficient to secure an interview. At the time of the interview, the main aspects of the difficulty can be reviewed. School records will, of course, contain notes of these interviews, the nature of the difficulty, the action proposed, and the effect observed.

In this way, the records and reports can be a vital part of school organization. They give a developmental picture that, in its construction, helps the teacher's understanding of the children, enriches his insights into human nature, and makes his observation of children more keen. They provide a mechanism whereby home and school co-operation may be placed on a sound basis.[7]

VII. DISCIPLINE AND PUNISHMENT

What Is "Discipline"? The word *discipline* comes from the same root as the word *disciple,* which means "a

[7] An excellent experiment in recording and reporting has been described in *The Educational Guidance of the School Child,* under the authorship of Professor Hamley and others (Evans Brothers, London, 1937).

learner." It therefore denotes a situation or set of conditions where learning, growth, and development can take place effectively. In general terms, as it applies to the school, we sense its more positive aspects when we contrast the older forms of school procedure with those advocated and increasingly adopted at the present time. The old, quiet, hear-a-pin-drop kind of classroom setting has gone into the discard. In its place the modern school encourages purposive activity, with children moving about in pursuit of their respective goals, conferring with one another; and the straight rows of desks are often replaced by tables and chairs, which lend themselves to group activity.

Discipline, of course, is not confined to the school. There is discipline in every respect of living. We cannot jump from the top of the Empire State Building without obvious consequences. Social rules and regulations "regulate" our behavior. We may drive on the left of the road if we wish; but there will be consequences different from those that accompany driving on the right. In nature, and in social groups, there are definite limitations to the chaotic freedom of impulsive behavior. We learn to adjust to the physical world by learning to understand and to obey its laws. We have to learn also to adjust to the rules of society by understanding them and respecting their purpose and contribution to group living.

Discipline in the school, therefore, is simply the means of ensuring that the ideal of the school may be maintained; or, in other words, that the teacher and class as a co-operative group, pursuing interests in various fields, may progressively learn to understand the workings of the physical and social worlds in which we live. It is but one aspect of group living.

The Objectives of Discipline. In the light of the above discussion of the nature of discipline, the objectives are clear: first, that classroom conditions shall be such that they assist the group as a whole in pursuing the tasks at hand; and second, that this shall be done in such a way as to promote in the pupils self-control and self-direction, and contribute to the enrichment and growth of personality.

The old repressive discipline did not do this; it did *not* promote self-control and self-development. Soldiers and sailors who have been under very severe discipline are not especially noted for self-control when on leave. Parents who have very repressive methods of discipline are likely to have disobedient children or children who go to extremes of behavior when restraint is removed.

The modern approach to discipline regards it from the angle of growth in group living and in the development of a balanced co-ordination of individual and group needs, making possible a maximum of constructive social participation. Discipline, therefore, in the sense of learning to live with others, under conditions that promote the interests of the individual and of the group, is not to be either ignored in school or regarded as a necessary evil. Rather, it is one of the prime objects of education and *not* a thing to be dismissed as soon as possible without planning or without thought. It is even more direct in its contribution to development than the material of the school subjects; for whatever subjects are taught, the setting in which they are experienced is all-important.

The old discipline failed because of its emphasis on punishment, which was meant to fit the offense, not the offender. The old rules, which were supposed to operate with the inevitability of the laws of nature, were supposed to be impersonal, and yet they affected the welfare of persons. While the old discipline often impressed on pupils the exact cost of a misdemeanor, it seldom got at the underlying cause of the trouble. It might merely drive the manifestation of the underlying difficulty into another channel. Usually, if the teacher succeeded in driving the manifestation of underlying emotional difficulty into channels outside the classroom, he was satisfied.

Today, with the mental-hygiene view of education, the development of efficient people with wholesome personalities is our objective. In the classroom this involves the diagnostic approach to the problems of discipline. It involves *understanding* the offender. It involves *treatment* on psychological and constructive lines—which means individual treatment. Many illustrative cases have been cited in previous chapters, but in order to throw into relief the difference between the old and the new concept of discipline, still another illustration may not be amiss.

A thirteen-year-old boy of normal physique and intelligence has lost all interest in his work. He is not troublesome, but he cannot be interested in the work of the class. The old method of discipline would have been content to label him "lazy," as exhibiting "lack of concentration," and would have applied pressure either by scolding or, after several warnings, by administering the strap. The new discipline, by seeking to discover the underlying cause of the difficulty, may reveal that he is emotionally upset because he feels that his father has no use for him. The father has a certain conception of what a typical boy ought to be interested in—athletics, scouting, and so forth—and the other two boys of the family fit this picture perfectly. This one does not, and has been made to feel his inferiority in this respect. The remedy is not the strap, but the actual righting of the relationship between father and son.

Punishment. Punishment is the completely negative side of discipline. In school settings we are familiar with corporal punishment, detention, extra assignments (not for practice, but as punishments—a procedure hardly likely to increase a child's enthusiasm for the subject concerned), ridicule, sarcasm, deprivation of privileges or of marks, scoldings, apologies, reporting to parents, and so on. These and other devices are supposed techniques of "enforcing discipline."

The underlying objective of the older type of punishment appears to have been one of retribution—an eye for an eye and a tooth for a tooth. This is psychologically unsound for two reasons. First, it is based on the assumption that every human action is the product of deliberate thought and plan, and that the pupil could just as easily have chosen the opposite course had he so wished. Modern studies deny the validity of this assumption in that they find it necessary to regard behavior as a complex product of many factors—physical, mental, social, and environmental—some of which have their roots far back in the history of the individual. Secondly, as a method of handling the child, retribution is likely to arouse antagonism, and so works against group co-operation.

Sometimes punishment is defended because of its value as a deterrent. This argument has some point if carefully interpreted. Usually, however, the fact that the deterrent aspect is stressed means that the positive side of the learning process is overlooked. It is easy enough to prevent a given form of behavior by making the penalty severe (provided, of course, that we can enforce the penalty). But how to train the individual along other lines, and how to determine what those positive lines are like —these are much more challenging problems; and they are the ones to which our traditional view of punishment contributed little or nothing.

Should there ever be a place for punishment in schools? Ideally, no. By that we do not mean that the children in an ideal setting would behave exactly as we wished at all times. But we should be able to understand the reasons for what they did, to the extent that we would then know how best to help them learn to solve their own problems of adjustment. This becomes clear as we consider the arbitrary nature of punishment. To this task we now proceed.

First of all let us look at the general problem of adjustment to the physical world. In our continuous and changing experience, our understanding of things develops considerably as we appreciate the outcomes resulting from our actions. Thus we learn that fire is hot, ice is cold, a razor is sharp, because, by placing our hand in the fire, we experience painful burning, and so on. There is, of course, something arbitrary, in a sense, in all this. But the outcomes resulting from our behavior follow in so consistent and orderly a way that we readily learn the meanings of these physical phenomena for our adjustment. They follow quite naturally. In other words, we see them as the necessary outcomes of our behavior.

In the social world it is difficult to set up so adequate a learning situation. The social consequences of stealing jam from the kitchen may not be at all similar on two different occasions. Even if we are "caught in the act" we may be reproved at one time, ridiculed at another, or even praised at another. The difficulty is to order a consistent social discipline that will make for ready learning. Because of this difficulty we often resort to arbitrary punishments, which at least indicate our displeasure concerning the act that is deemed to deserve punishment, but do very little, if anything, to point the way to positive social behavior. Because punishment is arbitrary, too, it tends to sidetrack the issue, so that the child learns to avoid being caught, or to overcome the punishment by resistance or subterfuge, or to resent the punitive action taken, and so on.

Let us review briefly some of the typical punishments that have at some time been familiar in school practice. Imposition of schoolwork, especially for general misbehavior, goes contrary to the teacher's desire to interest the pupil in the work itself. Even when imposed because of the child's failure to complete an assigned task, there is often the chance that the task was beyond the child's capacity or training. The situation could have been avoided by more careful planning or by training the child to work at his own pace and to experience the satisfaction of achieving at his maximum rate, to stick to something that is difficult for him for the sake of mastering it, and so on. Detention in school, with or without the imposition of schoolwork, similarly works against our desire that the child should learn to be intelligently interested in the school and its activities. Punishing pupils by making them do tasks for the good of the group as a whole (for example, sweeping the floor, flooding the rink, and so forth) works against the goal of their finding satisfaction in contributing to the happiness of the group. Deprivation of privileges is a better form of punishment, but not when manifest unfairness enters into the situation, as, for example, when academic marks are deducted for bad behavior. Sarcasm and ridicule have no place in the schoolroom, for few teachers can use them without a sting, and the blow to the child's ego may be serious.

Further, such practices are frequently quite unjust, and they lead to an unfortunate antagonism between teacher and pupil, which may inhibit the child's participation in the life of the group or lead him to get compensatory satisfaction in ways directed against the teacher's authority. Reproof, rebukes, scoldings, dark looks are negative in their influence. Positive substitutes could so readily be found. In any case, if the former seem, on occasion, to be necessary, they should be swift and straightforward, with an immediate resumption of the co-operative spirit. In no case, however, can they be thoroughly justified in positive terms. The list could be continued at great length.

Perhaps a word should be added about corporal punishment—including not only "strapping," but also even worse practices, such as "standing in a corner," and so forth. It obviously indicates a weakness somewhere. Education used to employ it a great deal, particularly when teachers were untrained and when the technique was rote memorization and periodic recitation. But there is very little use of the strap nowadays. Where it is used frequently, there are often unusual features in the community life or in the emergency situation; or else the teacher is weak, professionally at least. The arguments against corporal punishment are sound; but there is little to be said for virulent argument against *any* form of punishment unless the philosophy is carried forward to point the way to a sounder, more positive discipline in education.

Where we have to use arbitrary regulators, such as rules, or arbitrary consequences, such as rewards or punishments, these should form a relatively small part of our system. We can get on with very few rules—much fewer than we often employ. And these few rules should be carefully enforced, should be meaningful to the child in the situation to which they apply, and should carry over, because of their obvious pertinence to the social situation at the time, to the general attitude of respect for the legitimate rules of the game that are framed in the interests of the group. If he is happy in the group, the child accepts the rules of the group or participates in a healthy way in their revision, as occasion demands. Punishment, if ever employed, should have the same social values in mind. Often an emergency situation calls for calm, immediate removal of the recalcitrant from the group, rather than for an emotional battle there and then. Indicating that *this* form of behavior cannot be tolerated is sometimes necessary. But the return to the group should have no hang-over from this incident. Rather, the child on returning should be given (not obtrusively) a measure of satisfaction that will go far in cementing him to the group and undermining any tendency to withdrawal or antagonism. Above all, each case for correction is an individual case; general principles of treatment must be applied in the light of individual needs.

The basic answers to questions of punishment and discipline all lie in the realm of more positive, insightful, carefully planned education, where individual needs are appraised, directed, and developed.

VIII. STAFF CONFERENCES

Staff meetings are often a formal nuisance. They deal with matters of detail, human enough in themselves, but sadly divorced from any real educational significance. Miss X has been ill; we should send her a bouquet of flowers as a sign of our sympathy and respect. The recently acquired wing or gymnasium involves us in extra regulations, which must be formalized, and so on.

Details of administration always demand staff co-operation. But the staff conference as a medium of advancing educational thought and perspective is so much more significant. Staff meetings at convenient intervals, where educational points of view can be discussed, questions of method raised, individual pupils and their needs investigated—these and allied considerations may be used as means of revitalizing the attitude of the staff and of keeping to the fore the real challenges of educational practice. Regulations regulate; but staff conferences can stimulate progress.

IX. SUMMARY

This chapter borders on the educationist's field. It concerns itself, however, with this central point: that educational policy may be determined largely by crystallized regulations laid down for all, or by flexible and artistic understanding of the needs of each individual child. Thus the curriculum can be standardized, the aim of education being to force each child into the same mold; or the curriculum is flexible, and each child is an activity center deserving of human attention in his own right. The grading system is based on the achievement of the average child (whose parentage no adult will accept!), or it is geared to the needs and potentialities of this child and that (whom everyone is proud to assist). The examinations are administered by the civil service in the interest of official standards; or they are based on the progress of each individual child. Records are designed in the interests of statistical tables, or in the interests of guiding individual children and their responsible sponsors.

Discipline is punitive, or educative. Staff conferences are puerile, or constructive.

Mental hygiene and education can never be in conflict so long as both are concerned with child development, inspiration, and guidance. Good education cannot be harmful to the mental well-being of pupils. Sound mental hygiene will never act contrary to the best educational procedures. The partnership between mental hygiene and education is obvious. In practice, that partnership can be effective only to the degree that both members are directed in their policies by a sound understanding of child nature, its needs and potentialities.

CHAPTER X

The Teacher

I. THE TEACHER LOOKS AT HIMSELF

We have seen that the developing personality of the child is influenced for better or worse by a wide variety of factors. His inherent mental ability or lack of ability, his physical health or disability, the individual circumstances of his home, his community, his family, and his friends, and, finally, the organization, administration, and curriculum of his school—all these play a part in determining whether the child's basic needs are met satisfactorily and legitimately or not. All these factors, therefore, influence the development of his personality.

We now turn to the one remaining major influence in the child's life, the teacher himself. We shall assume that the teacher is a good teacher, from the more formal educational point of view, that he has acquired an adequate knowledge of his subject matter, and that his teaching methods and skill are without question. His function comes within the scope of this Manual, however, at the point where such matters as the following are at issue: Does he make his subject vital, living, a worth-while human experience, or is he a mere purveyor of information, a skilled artisan, yet lacking in inspiration? Does he, by his personal qualities and understanding of other people, make experience and achievement in his field of real interest to his pupils? Is he living his job—in his professional relationships, in his social relationships with the communities outside and inside the school? Is his sense of security adequate, so that he can give his attention to making the high contribution demanded and made possible by his function; or is he insecure, with a consequent tendency to be at war with others—even his pupils? Are his relationships to educational and other social authorities sound? Is his mental health such that his contribution to the education of our children will be wholly positive? Has he that freedom which we are nowadays demanding for the child—freedom to pursue his development along lines that will contribute to his personal and social endeavors? Is he exercising the privilege of the freedom now granted to him as fully as he might? Are there problems of teacher training and selection at issue in these matters—problems over and above those which involve knowledge of subject matter and clearness of presentation?

The mental health of the teacher is important to himself and to others with whom he comes in contact—colleagues, pupils, other friends and associates. It is, of course, especially important to those with whom he lives most intimately—which again includes himself.

If the antiquated system in schools still obtained, where the teacher was simply an imparter of information, provided he performed that task without displaying his personality unduly, his mental health would largely be his own business as far as the classroom is concerned. It is true that poor mental health would mean lower efficiency even in the routine of teaching facts. But he might "get by" sufficiently to satisfy the supervisor, and produce "examination results" in his class sufficient to avoid undue censure or comment. Under these conditions his colleagues and his intimate friends might still be concerned about his poor mental health; but the pupils would not be very closely related to him socially, since he would be functioning as a talking machine. When the children had to be "disciplined," if they did not see fit to do exactly as he commanded, or did not learn as rapidly as he expected, his personality would be more likely to influence the classroom picture. And in so far as it is weak, his influence would be undesirable also.

But in the modern picture of education, the teacher's mental health is very definitely of interest in regard to its influence on the children; for our classrooms are extremely socialized, and the children are numbered among the teacher's intimate associates. There can be no inspiration, no communication of enthusiastic interest in the subjects discussed by the teacher, unless the children participate intimately with one another and with him in these fields of activity.

The Influence of the Teacher's Personality on Children. For several reasons we would hesitate to draw the parallel between contagious physical disease and the influence of the teacher's personality on the pupils. Even if we had here in mind the occasional occurrence of frank mental disease among the still-practicing teachers, the parallel would be unsound; for, while none of us would want our children to be placed under the direction of such a teacher, the influence that would result could in no sense be regarded as one of contagion. We cannot "catch" mental disability in any sense of the word; and any attempt to stretch the meaning of *contagion* to make it an apt simile in our present discussion could only render that discussion subject to ridicule or gross misunderstanding.

The only point we need emphasize is that a teacher who is not well-adjusted and reasonably mentally healthy and who is unable to do his best work cannot be an effective director of the thought and activities of a socialized class and does not present an example of human living that we hope our children will achieve. Where temper or bullying, for example, are techniques used by a teacher in trying to make his pupils conform to some standard that he demands, the influences will be undesirable. The pupils are not thereby learning better techniques of social co-operation. They may learn to accept these undesirable techniques as patterns for solving their own problems of adjustment. Either by failing to learn acceptable forms of behavior or by learning undesirable forms, the child suffers in his development.

The teacher with faulty personality development may have other traits which are equally unfortunate as far as the pupils are concerned. He may be inconsiderate, impatient, prejudiced, rigid, or unimaginative; he may be sarcastic and overcritical; he may have an unpleasant voice, appearance, or manner; he may place too great an emphasis on grades, competition, and punishment; or he may simply be a colorless individual, completely lacking in physical vigor. Many teachers are unable to become effective leaders of children because of their extreme sensitivity and inherent lack of confidence in themselves. Just as the child may overcompensate for his feelings of failure and inferiority, so may the teacher, with even more devastating results. Rivlin [1] refers to the teacher who, feeling insecure in his professional duties, interprets as a challenge many of the normal, but unpleasant, characteristics of children. He describes the "almost hysterical efforts of the teacher who misinterprets the lack of

---

[1] Rivlin, H. M., "The Personality Problems of Teachers," *Mental Hygiene*, 23:1-12, January, 1939.

interest as impertinence, and stupidity as misconduct. He then threatens, scolds, punishes, coaxes, drills, and coaches—in short, he does everything but teach."

Such a teacher finds it very difficult to "take criticism," and is very often prone to interpret as deliberate persecution the efforts made by supervisors to offer helpful suggestions.

Studies of Teachers' Personalities. In a recent survey of many of the school systems in New York State,[2] a wide difference in the personalities of teachers was discovered. The personalities seemed to vary with the schools and school systems and with the attitudes of the different administrative heads. Thus a tendency was discovered for the principal of "broad vision with an understanding of human values" to select teachers with such vision for his staff. These teachers were contrasted with those in schools where the administrators were egocentric, prejudiced, unimaginative, and so on. The report goes on to state in detail: [3]

"In some schools both the principal and the majority of the teachers possessed warm understanding and a real capacity to relate themselves to pupils so that the entire group of students eagerly participated in the lesson at hand, and evidently derived considerable satisfaction from their achievement.

"In other instances there was an outstandingly poor relationship between principal, teachers, and pupils, evidenced by an impersonal attitude of detachment and a lack of real interest on the teacher's part in the individual pupils or in the educational material. Teachers and pupils alike accepted the situation either with boredom or with active annoyance. A large number of teachers were observed who evidently conceived

[2] Winslow, C. E. A., *The School Health Program* (Report of the Regents' Inquiry), McGraw-Hill Book Company, New York, 1938.
[3] *Ibid.*, page 26.

their role to be that of a disciplinarian and drillmaster, and maintained authority by the use of sarcasm, nagging, ridicule, and dogmatic domination."

If teachers' personalities are so important in their influence on developing children, surely efforts should be made to determine something about the personalities of teachers already in service. Many attempts have, in fact, been made to study the personalities of large groups of teachers and, as would be expected, the task has been found to be very difficult indeed. While surveys of the physical health of teachers-in-training and teachers-in-service have been made without much difficulty, it has been extremely difficult to make a survey of the same teachers in respect to their mental health and personality. Mental health implies something that is very personal to us. We are apt to resent as impertinence any attempt by a stranger, no matter how competent or how scientific, to assay the soundness of our personality. Nevertheless, Peck [4] studied the personalities of a hundred women teachers in a university summer course during 1935. On the basis of the Thurstone Personality Schedule one third of the teachers were "definitely maladjusted," while one sixth needed psychiatric advice. While we admit that the findings of such a survey are unconvincing, because of the lack of validity of the measuring tools employed, nevertheless such findings are food for thought.

II. THE IDEAL PERSONALITY FOR THE TEACHER

It is easy enough to criticize. It is also easy to describe and even caricature unfortunate aspects of certain teach-

[4] Peck, L., "A Study of the Adjustment Difficulties of a Group of Women Teachers," *Journal of Educational Psychology*, 27:401, September, 1936.

ers' personalities. But what, after all, constitutes the ideal personality for a teacher? Does such a personality exist in reality? If it does, can this type of personality be deliberately developed among our teachers-in-training and teachers-in-service?

A careful survey of scientific opinion on this point can be boiled down to a very simple statement. Obviously, it would be most unwise to countenance for a moment the idea of turning out from our training colleges teachers with a definite, set type of personality. The whole point of the newer freedom in education emphasizes the development of a healthy individuality among both teachers and pupils. There are certain characteristics of healthy personality development, however, which all teachers should have. Rivlin [5] describes these characteristics in the following terms:

"First, there is professional zeal, with interest in the process of education and the ability to continue his mental and professional growth while he is on the job. Second, there is a conviction that education is significant and that in the process of education his is an important role. Third, there is a sense of self-assurance and self-confidence which leads him; to recognize the problems growing out of his work and to feel that he will ultimately be able to solve them. Fourth, he responds to intelligent criticism without being offended or feeling unduly sensitive. Finally, he treats his students calmly and impartially without projecting upon them his own biases and prejudices or using them as a means of solving his own emotional problems."

An examination of these desirable traits will show that almost the same characteristics are desirable in any profession or occupation and that, indeed, they are a description of the well-developed, healthy personality. A com-

[5] *Op. cit.*

parison of these traits with the norms of personality, development described in Chapter II [6] will verify the statement that what the teacher really needs is a *normal* personality. Similarly, the faults described in the previous sections would be a handicap in any line of endeavor. So there are very few, if any, typical personality disabilities among teachers. Certainly there should be no typical *teacher's* personality.

A discussion of desirable personality traits for teachers inevitably leads to a consideration of the training and selection of student teachers. Unfortunately, there is no truly valid test for personality which might be used in this important work. Nor is there any sure method of training students or teachers in the field, so that they tend to develop these important qualities. This does not mean to say that no serious efforts have been made to investigate the possibilities of adequate selection on the basis of personality. But, so far as the authors know, there is no short-cut routine method of doing this. The most successful and meaningful student selection programs are based on careful clinical appraisals, together with extensive psychological and educational tests and evaluations.[7]

III. PERSONALITY PROBLEMS AMONG TEACHERS

We have intimated above that the teacher's mental health and personality is of primary importance to himself. If the teacher's personality falls far short of what would be considered adequate and normal, then, cer-

---

[6] See page 11.

[7] The National Committee for Mental Hygiene (New York) has issued a series of bulletins entitled "Education and Mental Health" in which various interesting and provocative experiences and experiments in the preparation and selection of teachers are described.

tainly, the teacher himself should be interested. Again, we would stress that we are not dealing here with the grossly abnormal or frankly unhealthy personality. We are concerned here with the common everyday difficulties which affect everyone's behavior. There is no evidence to show that the teaching profession is more likely to cause mental strain than any other profession, or that teachers need psychotherapy any more than do other citizens. Neither are we concerned with the need for self-appraisal on the part of the teacher. Every adult should realize that any deviation from perfect mental health represents a loss in personal well-being and social efficiency; that mental health is not something we achieve and then possess forever, any more than is physical health; that securing and maintaining an increased degree of mental health necessitate care and effort; that self-appraisal and gaining insight into our own mental-health status are commonsense procedures and do not necessarily lead to morbid introspection. We should all appraise our personal happiness, not seeking it directly, but arranging our lives so that by our achievements and daily contacts we enjoy a goodly measure of satisfaction. We should all cultivate a greater breadth of vision in regard to social relationships and human values, a calm, purposive consistency in our behavior, a wide and satisfactory set of interests, a measure of promptness in making decisions and a readiness to accept the consequences of our behavior. These things concern us all—not merely the teacher.

The fact that the teacher is dissatisfied with his own personality development, that he realizes something is wrong with himself or his job, indicates that he already has a degree of insight which is the first prerequisite for changing things for the better. Perhaps the teacher can be objective enough to apply the "diagnostic approach" to himself. He can be assured that no improvement in mental health or personality can be expected until the causes of the difficulties have been located. Certainly a healthy personality cannot be acquired by reading a book or going to a mental-hygiene lecture.

The cause of personality difficulties among teachers can usually be found in one or more of three spheres—the teacher's personal life, his professional life, and his relationship to the community.

Problems in the Personal Life of the Teacher. The teacher, like any other citizen, is not immune to problems and difficulties in his own personal life. These problems commonly concern his health, his financial status, and his domestic relationships. Obviously, the teacher who is worried about serious reverses on the stock market, who is constantly thinking about the possible necessity of a thyroid operation, or who is overly concerned about the difficulties of his domestic situation will find it difficult to shed completely these worries when he enters the classroom. After all, the teacher, like the pupil, cannot be divided into a schoolroom part and an out-of-school part.

Unfortunately, many teachers who show signs of difficulties, disappointments, and frustrations in this personal sphere are not able to solve these problems, or even to approach them, logically and dispassionately. The danger is that their personalities become so set and rigid that it seems as if a barrier exists between the cause of the trouble and the possible solution. Without becoming too introspective, the teacher must learn to take stock of himself, his personality, and his problems. He must, above all, cultivate an objective point of view. He must get to *know himself,* recognizing his own assets and liabilities, his aspirations, and his limitations. Emotional problems cannot be successfully dodged forever. There are certain facts and situations which exist for us all that simply must be faced and accepted. The single lady teacher over thirty-five must accept as gracefully as she can the fact that her chances of matrimony are slight. The middle-aged teacher concerned about his failing health and increasing signs of fatigue and lack of energy should endeavor to do something about it. Constantly worrying about his condition, hoping against hope that next week will see an improvement, or that a vacation will cure the trouble, will leave him emotionally and mentally exhausted, totally unable to meet even his own problems, let alone the problems of the classroom. In cases of this kind a physician should be consulted at once. If there is nothing seriously wrong the teacher will be greatly relieved and helped. If there is something wrong, the sooner he gets it corrected the better.

There is a great deal to be said for the appointment of a psychiatrist to the school system, whose duties will include, in addition to his supervising psychiatric work with children, personal work with teachers if they so desire.[8] Such a specialist is usually able to approach the teachers on a friendly but impersonal basis. He does not represent authority, as do the supervisors or the principals. The teachers may have confidence that a friendly discussion with the psychiatrist will result in no discrimination against them. The problems discussed will naturally be strictly confidential. The following case illus-

8 Such a system is described by Carleton W. Washburne in *Understanding the Child,* June, 1937, page 3.

tration indicates how this friendly relationship between the psychiatrist and the teacher can sometimes work out well for all concerned:

A middle-aged principal had been called upon by his Board of Education to account for the fact that the number of corporal punishments in his school had increased steadily over the last three years. It happened that the school psychiatrist was doing some work with a few of the children in this school, and one morning he made a point of taking time off to pay a friendly visit to the principal. The conversation turned naturally to the problem of the moment; and the principal described in no uncertain terms how he felt about the Board's interference. "This school is a large school, as you know," he said, "and it is in one of the worst districts of the city. If you don't keep right after these young roughnecks and scare some good sense into them, you will have them playing truant and coming late all the time." He proceeded to become more and more excited about the whole problem; and he took the opportunity to "blow off steam" about a lot of other things, such as the way teachers were being trained nowadays, the "softness" of the family welfare agencies, the "ridiculous" new changes in the curriculum, and so forth.

The next day the psychiatrist went in to see him again. The principal intimated that he would like to chat about his own twelve-year-old daughter. He was obviously quite disturbed and worried about her. It appeared that the school physician had diagnosed an obscure heart condition and had advised prolonged rest in bed. This was a specially hard blow to the principal, because he had lost a young son two years previously through rheumatic fever complicated by heart disease. To make matters worse he was constantly quarreling with his wife, and his home life was becoming increasingly unhappy. He was not only worried about his daughter's physical health, but he viewed with great concern the constant supervision she would now have to receive from her mother.

"She'll make her hate me before she's through. I tell you I would take the child and leave town if I could only get away."

The psychiatrist received this information sympathetically. The principal himself stated that he felt better now that he had told someone about these troubles, which had been bothering him for so long. The psychiatrist suggested an evening at bridge. This was arranged for the next evening; and, in addition to the principal, two other teachers were invited. Talk, inevitably, turned to problems of education. The other teachers expressed interest in the mental-hygiene approach to discipline. The possible relationship between retributive punishment, vindictiveness, and emotional problems in the personal life of the teacher was discussed. The principal warmly maintained his reactionary attitude in the argument, but indicated that he was willing to read and discuss some of the newer literature in this field.

In the weeks that followed there was noticed a considerable lessening in the number of the corporal punishments administered at this school. The principal, true to his word, did considerable reading, and, while his attitude is still very conservative, there is no doubt that he has become more moderate. As far as his own emotional life is concerned, although circumstances have not improved materially, he has tried consistently, with the support and encouragement of the psychiatrist, to face his problems realistically. He has established wholesome social and recreational outlets, is far happier than he has ever been in the last five years, and is no longer "taking it out on the kids," to use his own expression.

Problems Relating to Professional Relationships. Our purpose here is to endeavor to analyze the teacher's professional situation, in order that we may indicate wherein that situation offers greater scope for effective and satisfying achievement, and wherein some of the difficulties of adjustment, too, are likely to be encountered. Some of the factors involved will naturally apply to other professions as well; but we shall stress especially those aspects which inhere in teaching.

In order to maintain wholesome relationships with his pupils, the teacher must enjoy a goodly measure of professional security. This security must come from a realization in practice of an adequate background of training, from possibilities for maintaining and enriching that adequacy, from wholesome social outlets appropriate to the professional status of the teacher, and from a reasonable safety of tenure and economic stability.

The question of training is partly the responsibility of the system in which the teacher is appointed. He has to qualify in accordance with certain set criteria, to undergo a defined program of training, and in these matters to accept the decree of his professional seniors without further ado. This is true in all professions. But whether he is inspired by his training college or not, his own professional security will depend a great deal on the attitudes toward his educational task that develop during his training and service in the field. No profession can stimulate and challenge its members if the training period is thought of as the final qualification for participation in that profession. Just as the entire outlook of medicine is one that fosters the notion of constant change, continuous scientific advancement, to which each practicing physician—as well as the research specialist—contributes, so in education the sense of progress is one of the first essentials to a healthy form of security. Security is never stagnation. The teacher needs the same experience of progressive achievement as does the child, in his own interest as well as in that of the child.

This sense of progress is never likely to come significantly from progressive financial returns. We might as well recognize that fact. Naturally a degree of salary advancement is legitimate, necessary, and worthy of being insisted upon. While professional organizations exist for far more than this one purpose, they nonetheless have an obligation in this regard that they should be prepared to meet. But the teacher should get behind his professional organization for reasons much more important than the question of salary alone.

Similarly a teacher's sense of progress may be fostered by progressive increase in his position in the hierarchy of responsibility. But this is very limited in scope, too. That hierarchy should never be viewed in terms of grades —as if teaching Grade Eight were a more responsible task than teaching Grade One—or even in terms of institutions, such as elementary schools, intermediate schools, high schools, colleges, universities, and so on. In most cases there are salary scales which suggest that the high-school teacher is a more important person than the elementary-school teacher, although no thorough-going educational point of view can justify this. If elementary-school teachers are prepared to demand the type and extent of training that will give due recognition to the responsibility of their important task, they can expect eventually to offset the illogical economic hierarchy that characterizes all our educational systems today. Again, progressive achievement is very rarely to be interpreted as getting out of one job and into another, requiring a different form of training—as, for example, in going from the position of grade teacher to that of supervisor. It is true that our supervisors should first have wide experience as grade teachers. But there are relatively few supervisors; and if all teachers strive for such "promotion," the educational field becomes highly competitive and belies its own ideals. Further, many teachers who were getting real satisfaction from their grade work or principalship have found the transition to the inspectorship a most difficult step; and often they have regretted such "promotion."

The important thing is progress in one's own job. The advancements to higher supervisory posts are fine when they are well directed and well chosen. But the teacher cannot be a thoroughly realistic and healthy human being if such avenues are the only ones that will satisfy his natural demand for personal progress.

Progress of the truly professional type involves a realization of the results of one's efforts and sees these results in a continuously enriched classroom experience with greater and greater understanding of children and increasing insights as to how the educational program can be fitted to meet the needs of children more adequately. In this process, stimulating contacts in reading, study, special courses, supervising children's camps, and summer-school work all assist. If real progress is to be continuous in education, it will come only through the efforts of teachers who are emotionally and intellectually secure in this sense and who are constantly making progress in their understanding of children.

Problems Relating to Community Relationships. With regard to the question of wholesome social outlets—while this is important to everybody, teachers need to cultivate its influences more than most groups. In this, they have certain handicaps. The community at large oscillates between two unfortunate extremes in its attitude to the profession. The old childhood awe of the teacher may at

times show itself in the lip-service and academic respect
shown to those who are "molding the lives of the coming
generation"; yet there is also the familiar economic
superiority of the "practical man," who prides himself
on being less bookish and more virile in the world of
affairs. Both attitudes—the one possibly a compensation
for the other—tend to place the teachers in a class by
themselves. Contributing to this tendency, also, is the
familiar intolerance manifest in so many communities in
connection with the teacher's life. Smoking, for instance
—even in men teachers—may be bitterly condemned.
Similarly, the use of make-up by lady teachers is often
taboo.

The only way to offset this tendency is for teachers to
be real citizens in every sense of the word. A wide range
of interests outside the classroom, friends in various
walks of life, a frank removal of inhibiting restrictions,
active contribution to and leadership in community life
generally are all excellent avenues for ensuring a measure
of healthful living and for building up a more worth-while
attitude to the profession among outsiders. Moreover,
teachers of this type are obviously the only ones that are
really qualified for their task in directing the development of children.

In addition to active social participation, the teacher
must not forget his own personal appearance in or out
of school. It is so easy for the schoolmaster to forget
about brushing and pressing his suit; and it is so often
convenient for the lady teacher to put on a drab brown
or black smock in school "to protect her clothes." If
smocks must be worn, let them be bright and colorful.
It is perfectly true that clothes contribute something of
value to personality. Not only will a neat and smart ap-

pearance help the teacher to achieve a feeling of poise and confidence, but it will be appreciated by the children in the class.

IV. TEACHERS AND PROFESSIONAL FREEDOM

We have mentioned some of these highly difficult and perhaps somewhat controversial matters, partly because of their intrinsic importance to a teacher's professional outlook, and partly to indicate to the beginning teacher the need for active participation in the counsels of his professional association. The mental health of the teacher is highly significant to him and to the effectiveness of his work. And a keen interest in all that concerns his profession is one of the strongest assets on the side of his own personal adjustment.

The whole tone of this Manual is based on the assumption that a large amount of freedom has been granted to the classroom teacher. When training regulations, curriculum, school boards, administrative edicts, inspectors, examination requirements stare the teacher in the face, there is a tendency for him to feel that this freedom is quite nonexistent. We would conclude this chapter by saying that while the administrators should constantly take more and more cognizance of the need for giving teachers a large amount of freedom, realizing that this is necessary for effective education and for progress beyond our present effectiveness, the teacher will also do well to recognize that he usually has far more freedom within his job than he is taking advantage of. Professional freedom —which is professional advancement in the sense indicated above—is a prime requisite of professional security. The more it is cultivated by the teachers, the more obvious will the possibility of its cultivation become.

CHAPTER XI

MENTAL-HYGIENE SERVICES AND THE SCHOOL

I. GUIDANCE AND COUNSELING

The Role of the Counselor in Elementary Schools. The terms *guidance* and *counseling* have been used with a variety of connotations. In most centers where counseling service is available in the elementary schools, the counselor represents a sort of liaison between the mental-hygiene bureau or clinic and the school administration. In some school systems, the visiting teacher acts in this capacity. The visiting teacher is a social worker as well as a teacher, and usually constitutes the ideal person for this type of service. The duties of the counselor will necessarily vary with the setting. In many school systems, it is arranged that one teacher in each school shall have special training in psychology, guidance, and counseling. This teacher can then act as a consultant for the other teachers. Frequently, he is able to suggest many practical measures of value in the way of remedial teaching or slight changes in curriculum that will more effectively meet the needs of individual pupils.

Organized counseling is more commonly encountered in high schools and teachers' colleges than in the elementary schools. In these settings, counseling has become a highly efficient and useful technique. Not only is the counselor available to students by appointment for a discussion about personality or academic difficulties, but also he is ready at all times to help the student organize his work and study habits, and even to discuss with him the very difficult problem of the selection of a vocation.[1]

One of the traditional uses of guidance and counseling is in helping the pupil with his vocational program. The existence of individual differences between pupils, differences in ability as well as personality, makes such guidance possible and occasionally necessary.

The Traditional Vocational-Guidance Program.[2] If we consider guidance as a matter that particularly concerns the teacher only when the child arrives at points in his career at which major decisions have to be made, we divorce it from the general field of education and make it the concern of the vocational-guidance specialists. At the same time, we render the task of such a specialist—if he may be supposed to exist in fact—an impossible one. Let us illustrate this further. A child, having climbed the ladder of our grade system of schooling, arrives at the stage at which he is about to leave school. For purposes of argument, let us suppose that the educational system has been concerned mainly with teaching a body of factual content, training the child to read, write, count, and so on, with relatively little regard for his personal peculiarities and special needs. The child has learned to like some of the things he has had to do, to despise others; and he seems to show abilities and interests in some activities, not in others. He is now to be given a certificate and sent out into the world with one of our educational

[1] For an excellent description of how such counseling services are organized in a teachers' training college, the reader is referred to the bulletins on *Education and Mental Hygiene* published by the National Committee for Mental Hygiene, New York. (See especially Bulletins No. 13, 15, 17, and 18.)

[2] A considerable portion of this section appeared in *Understanding the Child,* October, 1939, and is reproduced here by kind permission of the editor.

hallmarks on him. (The argument would be the same whether the diploma is high-school entrance, matriculation, B.A., M.A., or Ph.D.) He asks our advice and guidance. What advice are we to give him?

We can, of course, tell him something about particular industries and professions. If he wishes eventually to enter law, medicine, or teaching, we can tell him what further courses he must take, how much his further training will cost. We can give him a general estimate of what he is likely to earn, how members of a given profession engage their spare time, what possibilities for initiative and advancement are offered, and so on. A few doctors or lawyers may come to school to tell the boys something about their work, and give them a chance to see what these professional men look like. Similarly with various branches of industry and commerce. Much interesting and useful information about what people do in the big world outside the school can be brought to the child's notice from one source or another.[3] As a thread in the fabric of our school program, it should be brought to his attention, in any event, whether as vocational guidance, as social studies, or as an aspect of the sciences and mathematics.

Suppose, now, the boy asks our advice further. He has no clear idea as to what he wants to do, and has had little opportunity of sizing himself up in terms of his fitness for this or that. What can we do? We can, of course, appraise his general intelligence, and we know something about his academic attainments, habits of work in school, morals, and personality. If he is bright, he may find the

---

[3] See, for instance, *Choosing Your Life Work,* Third Revised Edition, by W. Rosengarten, McGraw-Hill Book Company, New York; George J. McLeod, Ltd., Toronto, 1936; also *Choosing Your Life Work,* a survey by the Alberta Teachers' Association, Edmonton, 1938.

professions or other lines of activity open to him. If he is average in intelligence, he may be better suited to occupations other than the professions. Such appraisal and direction is very helpful, if tactfully done and provided that there are no personal or parental prejudices or preferences to be overcome. Intelligence standards for given occupations are often useful.

How can our advice be made more specific? In answer to this question, the special-test enthusiasts have often stepped in with great spirit. Certain jobs or fields of work have been "job analyzed." They can be said to involve certain skills, certain special aptitudes, and certain types of social relationships. The recluse may still fit into the solitary artist type of work without being unduly hampered by his lack of social training. The mechanically adept boy may find his niche in the workshop, even though he did not do very well in the academic subjects. Analyze the job, measure the individual's aptitudes; choose a job that requires the sort of aptitude profile this individual appears to have, and you have avoided the square-peg-in-the-round-hole phenomenon. So runs the story, in its bare essentials. It is true the pupil then has to find an appropriate vacancy; but he is well labeled and duly guided!

Limitations of This Program. The more we consider this type of guidance, the more inadequate and narrow in outlook it appears. Undoubtedly there is some place for appraising a child's abilities and analyzing jobs to see what abilities they involve. Criticism involves rather a criticism of education than opposition to job specialists. The latter have appeared because education has failed precisely at this point. In the first place, the main stream of schoolwork has been divorced from an important aspect of the child's life and needs; namely, finding a suitable vocational interest, the base from which his operations as a citizen have to be conducted. Education has reserved, until the child is just about to leave school, its efforts to acquaint him with vocational possibilities. Any familiarity he has gained with industry, commerce, and the professions has resulted from incidental, undirected experience.

We may look at this criticism in another way. In an effort to analyze the student's capabilities, to see what sort of vocation he appears to be fitted for, we rely upon a few short tests, when actually we have been working with him in school for years! If the student must ask education what he can or should do to earn his living, obviously education has not given him much opportunity to find out for himself what his capabilities are. His schoolwork has given him an intensive training in the abstractions of school subjects, but little opportunity to explore his own interests and aptitudes in diversified lines of achievement.

This point of view does not imply that education must forsake its function of general development. Allowing the child to explore avenues of potential interest from which a vocation may be selected actively promotes strength of character and healthy personality.

Tests used by vocational advisers always suggest that personal aptitude is static in nature. They often imply that an individual is born with possibilities for greatness along some narrow lines, but inevitable stupidity along others. They "profile" [4] the student; and there he is,

---

[4] When scores obtained by an individual on a battery of tests are plotted graphically, one under the other, on a specially prepared record blank, the result is frequently referred to as a "profile."

fixed for all time as this or that type of person: the mechanically apt, the abstract thinker, the musical genius, and so on, categories reminiscent of the "head readers." Yet, as far as we know, all special "gifts" are the result of hard and intensive achievement. There are *some* bases that resist the influence of our training procedures, it is true. Short, stubby fingers are not equally as conducive to excellence in piano playing as are long, supple ones, especially since we seldom think of adjusting the size of our keyboards to fit individual cases. Voice characteristics are partly dependent upon organic features. A deformed face does not readily suggest itself as a recommendation for motion-picture fame, if public taste demands the Jean Harlow and Rudolph Valentino types. But apart from such obvious reservations, we can affirm quite confidently that special aptitudes depend so largely upon training that any innate influence on them should not be stressed. (The behaviorists denied the innate influences altogether, for the reasons we have outlined.) General capacity is something we have to accept as largely beyond our control. But in the matter of using and directing that capacity, fostering it along special lines, the whole atmosphere is one of optimism and challenge. Special abilities are the outcomes of education; if not in school, then elsewhere.

This point of view means that an individual's "profile" may change from time to time. The fact that the student seems apt in some directions now does not preclude the possibility of the development of other aptitudes later. The static view of personal fitness does not bear inspection.

Similarly, the static view of "jobs" does not bear inspection. Suppose, for example, we find that teachers have an I.Q. of 115 on the average. Does this mean that the average I.Q. of the teaching profession was always 115, or that it cannot be raised to 125 by more careful selection, improved professional standards, and so on? A person with an I.Q. below a given level probably should not be allowed to qualify as a teacher. But why not think of the profession in terms of attracting the brighter people, rather than of excluding the duller ones, and make the profession so challenging that only the more able can meet the challenge? Or again, suppose a given job demands a certain speed of reaction, a high acuity of vision, and a definite proficiency in a number of special forms of activity. If that job is narrow in scope, routine in nature, mechanical after the first few months, what is likely to happen if a human soul, apt as it is, is kept at that same job for twenty-five years? Will the personality as a whole maintain the same form, even though the reaction time, visual acuity, and special skills survive the test? Any job, any profession, is constantly changing to an individual, by the very fact that it is engaged in by a human being.

The question of guidance, therefore, is not merely fitting, at a given time, a person to a job, both the person and the job being regarded abstractly as made up of certain specialized skills, aptitudes, or demands. It is a matter that concerns the whole field of education. The records and reports, discussed in the previous chapter, symbolize the breadth and significance of *education as guidance;* and no narrow conception will suffice.

There is, of course, always a place for careful, analytical appraisal of an individual at a given time, especially when a decision has to be made regarding his fitness for a given situation. At this point, analysis of the personality is important. But suitability at any one time is only part of the story. The individual must appreciate the job in terms broader than any immediate job analysis, for he has to live his life in and around that job, and he has to live with other people, perhaps compete with them, certainly co-operate with them. If, through the influences of school, home, and community, the student's social and emotional development are inadequate, skills and special aptitudes are of little use.

Guidance as Education. Education realizes all this today as it never did before. It has resisted any ready-made, artificial solution to the guidance problem and has buckled down to a careful appraisal of development from the earliest years. Various special-guidance techniques are employed at different levels, and they become more highly specialized in the upper reaches of our educational system. But the special techniques (which often seem so prominent that they appear to *be* the guidance movement itself) are in reality a mere fraction of the total guidance mechanism, namely, the entire educational program. The child is given more and more opportunity for exploring himself, for learning to know by experience where his interests and aptitudes lie and to become acquainted with the meanings and values of various forms of human behavior.

It might not be too bizarre a vision if we should prophesy a time when schools would drop most of their academic program in the upper elementary-school course, and extend considerably the present-day opportunities for diversified activities. The return to the more academic subjects later would be more meaningful, more highly motivated; and in any case the child would have had a chance to learn many skills and crafts that would stand *any* citizen and householder in good stead.

Finally, the teacher, in consultation with colleagues and parents, is now trained more and more to be on the alert regarding direction of interests, seeing to it that a child does what interests him because his interest has been subtly directed into channels that prove to be worth while for him, to lead pupils to a more intimate understanding of economic and social institutions, and to exploit strengths and worthy attainments whenever they are discovered. As this trend in modern education becomes strengthened, teachers generally will be able to make a progressively more vital contribution to guidance as a directing force in education. For, while the teacher is essentially a leader and a guide of children, understanding and helping them, he also sees to it that the children are more and more able to guide themselves, in the face of success and disappointment, in attaining and maintaining satisfactory human relationships, in finding reasonable satisfactions in everyday activities and accomplishments, in making the transition from the somewhat artificial scholastic pursuits to those of the actual world of leisure and vocation.

II. TEACHING MENTAL HYGIENE TO THE CHILD

Such a "guidance program" is also a program of mental hygiene. It represents, indirectly, the approach of mental hygiene to classroom curriculums and procedures. The direct approach has had frequent reference in these pages in the discussion and illustration of unwholesome behavior. A second aspect of the direct approach refers to a procedure for teaching mental hygiene as one might teach health, social living, or other aspects of the curriculum. But can mental hygiene be *taught* positively, and without any ill effects?

As adults, we recognize that all children must face difficulties, meet responsibilities. We try to anticipate their needs in this regard by appropriate training at each age level. Our courses of study stress the necessity of teaching healthful living. Reduced to specific treatment, healthful living as a school "subject" is sometimes described in the curriculum as teaching "right attitudes toward work, rest, play, and study; toward home and community; toward the daily program; toward the interests of others." [5] No matter how anxious a teacher may be to have his pupils learn healthy attitudes or show such evidences of healthful living as frankness; absence of fears, of suspicion, of worry, and of unjust criticism of others; willingness to accept responsibility for one's own acts; and the other characteristics of healthy personality,[6] he is, nevertheless, faced with great difficulty when he attempts to teach such principles to his pupils directly. They are best acquired as by-products from other school activities. Consequently, there is need for considering how mental hygiene might be taken directly to the child, without waiting until he becomes recognizably disturbed or reveals to us signs of warped or unhealthy development.

Many psychological theories concerning personal peculiarities and abnormal forms of behavior are definitely unsuited to child consumption. Indeed, there is often danger, even with adults, of morbid introspection and self-analysis, when a little knowledge of some of the theories has been incorporated into emotional thinking. This type of pitfall must be avoided.

At the elementary-school level all that should be attempted in the way of "mental-hygiene teaching" is to al-

[5] *Courses of Study, Grades IX and X,* Health and Physical Education, Province of Ontario, page 8.

[6] See "Norms of Healthy Personality Development," page 11.

low the child to experience as many different types of social situations as possible. Without learning anything about "frustration" or "inferiority complexes" the child, through his activities in dramatics, for example, can gain practice in meeting social requirements, in overcoming disappointments, in giving place to others, and in doing the job for the "job's sake." Almost every division of the schoolwork has undoubted mental-hygiene possibilities when looked at in this way. Particularly valuable, however, are the less formal parts of the curriculum and the manner in which the activities are staged by the school. As examples, the following typical experiences are cited:

(*a*) In a school where a considerable amount of bullying was developing, the principal called the ringleaders into his office and chatted with them about a lad he knew who was continually annoying younger children. The principal explained the circumstances of this case, particularly those features of background which seemed directly to contribute to the difficulty: the older brother who bullied this lad at home and was, in turn, bullied by the father; the constant fear and strain under which the lad lived; and so on. He suggested that these boys be on the lookout for similar behavior in the playground, discussed with them how they might assist the boy in question, and gave them a definite feeling of understanding and responsibility.

(*b*) A boy of thirteen who was particularly shy and retiring, uncomfortable in social relationships, was rapidly becoming the object of the jibes of his classmates. The teacher, noticing this, called a few of the more responsible ones aside and explained the unfortunate nature of the boy's recessivism; he asked for their co-operation. These boys had never thought of the lad's behavior as being anything in the nature of a problem. They began to scheme out ways and means of bringing the boy into social activities. The techniques attempted varied from the rather naïve method of coaxing and cajoling, to the more subtle and indirect method of engineering the boy's election as convener of a committee to organize a party. The unofficial "socializing committee" reported progress from time to time to the teacher; and these meetings were utilized for making further plans. Before long the boy had become an acceptable and enthusiastic participant in most of the activities of the group. The boys responsible for the change in the trend of this lad's personality development had become enthusiastic observers of human nature. No attempt was made to teach them anything about the psychology of "fear," "withdrawal," "retreat," and so on. Nevertheless, the experience was a valuable mental-hygiene lesson for them.

(*c*) Still more positive in outlook is the frequently encountered attempt on the part of the school to give children a sense of responsibility and understanding in regard to younger children, as well as those of their own age or grade. The manual-training program may involve the older boys in visiting some of the junior grades, watching their classroom interests and enterprises, deciding how they can contribute. If in grades two or three co-operative pictures are being drawn to illustrate or interpret a story, easels can be made. It is fascinating to watch the big boy or girl who has thought of the very young child only as a nuisance, or as something that belongs elsewhere, suddenly taking an interest in understanding how he can contribute to the young child's needs; or, similarly, how he can contribute to the needs of an older person.

(*d*) One of the most interesting of the newer techniques devised for teaching children to think objectively about their own attitudes and family relationships is that which has been developed and demonstrated so successfully by Dr. Alice V. Keliher and Dr. Caroline Zachry. While this method is usually tried with high-school students, it is possible that it might be applicable to the senior grades in the elementary school. In the technique as demonstrated by Dr. Keliher, a sound moving picture is first shown to the class. This picture deals with an incident in the life of a boy of twelve. He gets into difficulties through misbehavior, and the subsequent relationships with adults is shown. Following the picture, an informal discussion takes place. The teacher guides, but does not dominate, this discussion. Cross-talk is encouraged. Questions are raised as to why the boy misbehaved. This leads to a discussion of various motives and why it is important to understand motives. This in turn frequently leads to a consideration of child-parent relationships and punishments. It is possible to guide the discussion into all kinds of avenues of intense interest to children of this age. The purpose is to stimulate them to think about these problems, to help them crystallize their ideas, and to review the logic lying behind these ideas and attitudes. Such discussions help children to think rationally and critically about their own behavior and their own habits of thinking, feeling, and acting. As demonstrated by Dr. Keliher, there is little danger of the discussion becoming too abstract or conceptual, or of its leading to unhealthy introspection on the part of the children. This technique of teaching "family relationships" or "healthful living" can be fitted easily into courses on household science and economics or health education.

In other words, whatever the setting, practical mental hygiene can be experienced by children of all ages. At the high-school level it is possible to guide discussion safely into such general topics as "family relationships." Much of the success of this, however, depends on the training, insight, and dramatic ability of the teacher. These are qualifications which can be obtained by any teacher. In the last analysis, the most important thing is that the teacher should acquire a complete understanding of children.

III. MENTAL-HYGIENE CLINICS

In spite of all efforts at counseling and guidance, and in spite of everything the teacher can do directly through the "diagnostic approach," or indirectly through planned activity, there will come to light every now and then children whose behavior is so unpredictable, unexpected, and so difficult to understand that expert assistance is required. In almost every community nowadays professional psychiatric and psychological services are available to teachers for just such emergencies.

Organization. The nature of the available mental-hygiene clinical services [7] varies in different parts of the country, and from city to city. Sometimes the clinic is part of the school health department, and sometimes it is part of the state or provincial health program. The personnel may be a single visiting teacher with special training in psychology and mental hygiene, or it may consist of a large staff of specialists, under the direction of a fully qualified psychiatrist. In any case, whether the clinic is part of the school health service or not, it is always willing to co-operate with schools and teachers in any serious effort to understand the problem behavior of children.

The typical mental-hygiene clinic is staffed by a psychiatrist, a psychologist, and a psychiatric social worker, together with clerical assistants. Where the case load is very heavy, there may be several psychologists and social workers attached to the same clinic. As a rule, the psychiatrist directs the clinic, decides the policies, and determines the therapeutic procedures necessary. In most clin-

[7] These clinics are called by various names; thus, Child Guidance Clinics, Habit Training Clinics, Behavior Clinics, Mental Health Clinics, and so on.

ics, however, the therapeutic procedures are decided upon only after a careful conference which enables information from the psychologist and the social worker to be pooled with that of the psychiatrist. Clinical policies are co-operative outcomes.

The Types of Services. When a mental-hygiene clinic is attached to the school system, many different types of services are provided. Study and treatment of children with difficult behavior or educational problems is probably the most important and most fundamental part of the work. These clinical services may be subdivided into various types. Only a small percentage of the children referred for examination require what is sometimes called a *complete psychiatric service.* In New York this type of service is given to about 25% of the children referred to the Bureau of Child Guidance.[8] A complete service includes a comprehensive investigation of the case from the social, educational, physical, and psychological points of view. The method followed is similar to, but more detailed than, that described in Chapter IV of this Manual. Included in the service is the more or less intensive psychiatric treatment of the child by the psychiatrist. Modern psychiatric research with children has discovered ways by which the child is enabled to "release" the emotional tension which contributes to his difficulties. Among these techniques are the various forms of play therapy.[9] The psychiatrist skilled in children's work is usually able to put himself on the same level as the child, to understand the problem from the child's point of view, and to become a friend and confidant of the child. The tech-

[8] Ciccarelli, E. C., "Educational Components in Clinical Child Guidance," *Understanding the Child,* January, 1939.

[9] Some of these play techniques are discussed in *Understanding the Child,* Vol. 7, No. 2, June, 1938.

nique varies, however, from case to case and from worker to worker.

Over two thirds of the children referred for mental-hygiene investigation do not require such complete investigations. In many cases the social background is already known to other agencies in the community; and with this start, the clinic can proceed with a great saving of time. Many children require only a psychological investigation, with suitable tests. In these it is a question of educational placement, or perhaps a specific subject disability. Here the psychologist is usually able to co-operate with the teacher in arranging the most effective remedial program. In many centers the psychologist is asked to supervise an extensive group-testing and grading program for some or all the schools. The psychologist may also have the responsibility of testing and selecting suitable children for special classes organized for children with limited mental ability or for children with other handicaps.

Many other services are provided by the mental-hygiene clinic attached to a school system. There are often heavy educational and community responsibilities. The members of the staff make a point of working directly and individually with the teachers of the children seen at the clinic. If a teacher follows the progress of one pupil through the clinical services, he is in a much better position to handle problems, by himself, when they arise. In addition to this individual work with teachers, however, discussion groups are often organized. These may consist of parents and teachers, or of teachers alone, depending on the circumstances. In these discussion groups, various aspects of the mental-hygiene services are discussed and illustrative cases presented. Occasionally, formal courses are organized for teachers, in which a more sophisticated program of instruction is presented. The clinic is also most anxious to co-operate with other social agencies of the community. Many of these agencies have well-trained social workers who can use the mental-hygiene clinic as a consultation center. In return, they help the mental-hygiene clinic by acting as liaison workers in the community.

Most mental-hygiene bureaus or clinics are interested in research. Mental-hygiene research in the schools is just beginning to take form. It is still largely concerned with "fact-finding" surveys. The highly significant Norwood School Project [10] is an excellent example of this type of research. This project, directed by Dr. Henry B. Elkind, is a co-operative enterprise, involving a group of workers in a public-school system in a community adjacent to a large city.

"The Project at Norwood contemplates a continuous study throughout the elementary grades, at least of one hundred children who entered the first grade in the fall of 1937. This number represents *all* the children, *with no exceptions,* in four first grades. This means that the observations and findings deal with the 'run-of-the-mine' child, so-called 'normals,' and not with abnormal cases selected for treatment or study.

"The Project itself has a number of objectives, the most important of which is the testing out in our public schools of the practical value of the mental-hygiene concept of the 'total child in the total situation.' In other words, can a practical, hygienic system be established in our public schools, with this idea as a guiding principle? At the present time, a great deal of the work done in our public schools for the adjustment of the individual child, if any such work is done at all, is divided among a number of divisions or departments, each operating

[10] An interim description of many aspects of this work is contained in *Understanding the Child,* Vol. VII, No. 3, October, 1938.

independently of the others, with no integrated approach to the individual child. This practice in itself violates the concept enunciated above."

A somewhat similar project is under way in the city of New York.[11] Psychological surveys are being made of entire grades (usually Grade One) to select children who are beginning to show signs of poor adjustment to school or faulty personality development. These amount to individual studies of all the children in the grade. Potential problems are revealed and remedial work begun here. In this way, the mental-hygiene program fulfills its ultimate purpose, namely, prevention.

Many mental-hygiene clinics are particularly interested in investigating the various techniques of remedial teaching. This applies to children who are having special trouble with certain subjects, such as arithmetic or reading. In other centers the research interest is more generally in the field of personality development. In several cities in Canada, for instance, a study is being made of children who are noticeably shy, timid, and recessive.[12] It has been noted that certain types of shy children respond well to the socializing influence of the classroom and the teacher.

Using the Clinic. The method by which a teacher or principal proceeds in order to make use of the mental-hygiene clinic varies, depending on the circumstances. In most communities, it is necessary to obtain the written consent of the parents before children are examined. When the clinic meets regularly in the school, referral is usually easy. All that is necessary is that the teacher

[11] Krugman, M., "The Psychologist in a Mental Hygiene Program," *Understanding the Child,* Vol. VII, No. 4, January, 1939.

[12] See *Understanding the Child,* April, 1939. A full account of these studies is to be published shortly.

notify the principal, who then may proceed with the arrangements.

When such clinical services are easily available to the teachers, there are certain dangers which must be avoided. One of these is the use of the clinic by the teacher as a "threat" to the child. The teacher or principal who threatens either the child or his parents with an examination by the mental-hygiene clinic is not only misinterpreting the purpose and function of this organization, but is indicating a complete lack of insight into the meaning of mental hygiene and the nature of the child's personality. Similarly, the teacher who regards the clinic as a "place of disposal" to which he can send all his difficult children, without assuming any further responsibility, is misunderstanding the mental-hygiene point of view. The teacher will always have responsibility in connection with his pupils. Inevitably, he forms a vital part of the therapeutic program.

Occasionally, antagonism arises between the educationist and the psychiatrist. Each becomes critical of the other. When this is the case, it is very difficult for the mental-hygiene clinic to work constructively in the school. Part of this antagonism may be due to a fundamental difference in the points of view represented by the psychiatrist and the teacher. The former may be chiefly interested in the study of the individual and his relationship to the group; the latter is often aware only of the individual natures of his children when they disturb the group. Another possible reason for antagonism is the fact that there is no other program in the school so likely to interfere with the regular teaching program and classroom procedure as the mental-hygiene service. Not only are children removed from the classroom for purposes of testing and examination, but also the therapeutic recommendations almost always involve extra work and individual attention to the child on the part of the teacher. Fortunately, this antagonism and difference in point of view is rapidly disappearing. As teachers learn more about the techniques of the mental-hygiene clinic, they become more sympathetic and interested in its work. There are many indications of this changing attitude of the teachers. When the mental-hygiene clinics first began to function in the schools, the children referred were sent either because they were "bad" boys, and had become involved in various forms of aggressive behavior, such as bullying, stealing, disobedience, and so on, or because they were children who were failing noticeably in their schoolwork and academic achievement. The majority of the children were boys between the ages of ten and fourteen. Now the picture has changed. True, the clinics still get a goodly number of problems of this type. But more and more the teachers are sending children who are quiet, shy, and recessive, and, curiously enough, they now refer just about as many girls as boys. There is, on the whole, a decided tendency, too, towards referring children at younger ages. Thus, the clinics are beginning to do effective work in the prevention of the more serious personality disorders seen in later life.

The change in the teachers' attitude is not one that has taken place overnight. When a new service, which demands a great deal of co-operation and thoughtful work on the part of teachers, is suddenly thrust upon a school system, it is only natural that opposition and misunderstanding arise. The teachers may rightly feel that they already have a sufficient burden of work without spending time out of school hours working with a child who is a constant problem in the classroom. Progress in establishing a co-operative working basis with the schools and the teachers is, therefore, necessarily slow. Nevertheless, teachers are beginning now to think of their pupils as individuals—each with his own background and his own destiny. In many instances, the educators are not only looking for help from mental hygiene, but are beginning to provide leadership in this field.

Where the greatest progress in co-operation between the staff of the mental-hygiene clinic and the teachers of the school has been made, it is found that the specialists of the clinic have gone out of their way to understand as completely as possible the point of view of the teacher. They have consistently endeavored to understand the teacher's problems and difficulties. By keeping in close contact with the teachers, and by encouraging the teachers to contribute to the business of making a diagnosis and to take part in case conferences, the clinic is able gradually to build up its prestige and usefulness.

When a child is referred to the clinic, the teacher is usually asked to write a report about him from the point of view of his progress and behavior in school.[13] Of even greater importance, however, is the opportunity provided by most clinics for the teacher to take part in the conference and discussion of the child. At this conference all aspects of the case are reviewed, including the physical and personality history, the social background, psychological examination, and the teacher's report. The teacher who takes part in such a discussion is amply repaid for his effort by the greater understanding of the child's personality and behavior which the conference provides. The following case illustrates this point:

[13] See Chapter IV.

A very bright Jewish boy of eleven years, I.Q. 123, was becoming an increasing problem in the classroom. He was described by his teacher as a "show-off and a smart aleck." He was continually seeking attention from pupils and teachers, and when he failed to get attention legitimately, he would try other means, such as smirking and laughing at his own foolish mistakes. Many notes were sent home. The mother was not able to understand what was happening. The boy's explanations were always plausible. When the mother visited the school and tried to explain to the teacher what had happened, the teacher scornfully ridiculed the boy's explanation as "a pack of lies."

The mother sought the advice of a mental-hygiene clinic. A social investigation showed that the family were originally fairly well-to-do. The father, however, was now unemployed, and the family was on relief. The mother had been very active in social and charitable organizations, but now she had retired from all such work. Both parents were extremely proud and were embarrassed at their present financial status. The mother, particularly, possessed an aggressive personality; and much in her manner and bearing suggested that her son was patterning his personality after hers. This boy was the older of two sons. The younger son was also bright, and also was a problem, in that he was suffering from "excessive nervousness," including restlessness and nervous tics.

When the social worker talked with the teacher about the boy, the difficulties seemed to become more and more serious. The teacher appealed directly to the children in the class to corroborate the fact that he was a troublesome boy. She was invited to come to a staff conference, at which all aspects of the case could be discussed. Both the principal and the teacher turned up. At the conference, a brief report was made by the various workers who had an interest in the boy. The physical, psychological, and social aspects were stressed. It was further revealed that up to the time the child had been referred to the clinic no one had bothered to try to understand *his* point of view. It was shown that really he was feeling very inferior most of the time. Some of the children had ridiculed his racial origin. He was not skillful at sports. He was trying in the only way he knew to maintain his self-respect. His mother's manner provided a perfect pattern.

Obviously, the factors contributing to this difficulty were coming from all sides. It was decided that the psychiatrist should talk to the boy in an effort to help him understand his own behavior. The mother was to be helped in the same way. The teacher agreed enthusiastically to co-operate in helping the boy achieve a healthier point of view and a more acceptable manner in the classroom. In this way the conference facilitated an intelligent understanding by all concerned. Instead of critical antagonism, the teacher began to demonstrate a real interest in the boy and his parents. She accepted the problem as one involving the mutual responsibility of school and home.

The contact between the clinic and the teacher is usually arranged by the psychiatric social worker. Often this worker herself has been a teacher. At any rate, it is her responsibility to supervise the treatment procedures. In every case, the clinic has constructive suggestions for the teacher, but sometimes these suggestions are a bit vague and nebulous. It is the duty of the social worker to convert these recommendations into concrete practical suggestions. The clinic may decide, for instance, that the child needs to have the opportunity of winning approval in legitimate but simple ways. The teacher may be asked to find little jobs in the classroom for the child to do. Sometimes the clinic forgets that there is a limit to such "little jobs." As one teacher-worker put it, "There is only one blackboard to clean." The social worker and the teacher, however, can usually work out together a treatment plan which is both practical and effective.

The rural teacher may feel that clinical services such as described above are definitely not available for him. In some cases this may be true; but the situation is often better than the teacher thinks. Most states and provinces now provide traveling mental-hygiene clinics, which hold sessions in the larger towns and cities at regular intervals. After consulting with his superior or inspector, the teacher can often arrange for certain children to be examined at one of these clinics. Failing this, the teacher should survey the resources of the district. Among the physicians practicing in the area, there are bound to be one or two who have had some psychiatric experience and who would advise regarding special cases.

We have endeavored in this chapter to describe briefly the various types of mental-hygiene services that are available in many of the school systems, together with arrangements frequently made for counseling, guidance, and the teaching of "mental hygiene" to children. Our purpose here has not been to encourage teachers to become mental-hygiene specialists but, on the other hand, to show that the mental-hygiene point of view is compatible with, indeed essential to, good teaching and sound education. There will always be children who present special problems of such a nature that the attention of the specialist is required. For these, clinical services and facilities are a great advantage. For the great majority of children, however, who have never been "problem cases" and who never will be, the important point to remember is that the teacher and the educative process can make signal contributions toward the development of sound mental health and vigorous, wholesome personality.

CHAPTER XII

EDUCATION AND MENTAL HEALTH

I. THE TASK OF THE SCHOOL

Throughout this Manual it has been the purpose of the writers to point up the mental-hygiene significance of the various educational procedures in the elementary school. In this last chapter we endeavor to review in perspective the positive contribution of the school in fostering wholesome development and sound mental health. At the risk of repetition, an attempt is made to trace the changing task of the school from early times to the present. Perhaps it is not out of place in this chapter to describe also, very briefly, some characteristics of the school of tomorrow.

The present-day task of the school is not difficult to define in general terms. Schools exist as co-operative partners with the home in the business of bringing up children and of directing the development of our youth for a longer and longer time as education takes on more and more responsibility. This statement calls for little discussion, since it arouses no great controversy. But in practice, because of lack of clarity regarding what is meant by "bringing up children" and "development," many variations in interpretation show themselves in different schools and at different times. For this reason the task of the school is often misunderstood. Accordingly, we must consider it further.

Until fairly recently the greater number of children never saw the inside of a school. They were brought up in their own homes, by their parents, with their brothers and sisters. Their education was largely informal. They learned a great deal concerning various crafts practiced in the home. Vocational, avocational, religious, social aspects of their training were all centered there. Frequently the boys followed the major craft of the father, cultivating also a wide range of usefulness and skill; the girls learned very readily the business of taking care of the home and many things pertaining to that important task.

Those for whom schools were available were largely of a different social stratum. School activities did not necessarily deal with the details of everyday life. Reading, writing, and computation were, of course, taught; but these were tools for the broader fields of literature, history, the traditional mathematics and classics. In many centers a fine cultural background was fostered, so that travel, diplomacy, leadership, letters, the arts could find an important and meaningful place in the lives of those who were well schooled. A classical tradition was the natural result of such educational evolution through the centuries.

This general situation, where the education of the masses stood in contrast to that of the relatively few, tended to maintain class distinctions, to perpetuate the *status quo*. But other movements—such as the Industrial Revolution, the rise to prominence of industry, the growth of democracy, the importance of the voice of the people in parliamentary representation, and the like—led to an increasing demand for school education for the masses. Homecrafts were being displaced by factory activities in large industrial centers. National wealth and commerce depended more and more on manufactured products. Schools were demanded, to take over some of the responsibility of educating the young of all classes, not only those of the wealthy so-called leisured class. Public education, supported by popular taxation, grew apace. What form would this education take?

The Classical Tradition. One factor influencing the form of mass education thus engendered would naturally be the existing scholastic and classical tradition. Abstract knowledge of the distant past, the classics, Latin, Greek, languages generally, would be prominent. Another factor would be the demands of industry, through which, indirectly or directly, state schools were being supported, at least in part. Hence the sciences—research in which was all-important to industrial refinement and progress— and mathematics became increasingly important. As far as people generally were concerned, there would always be the need for reading, writing, and counting, in harmony with the notions of popular franchise, wage earning, and so on.

All these influences are apparent in present-day education and in popular attitudes toward education. Until quite recently the curriculums of our schools have very definitely reflected the classical tradition to an overwhelming degree. Democracy has demanded equal rights and privileges for all and has interpreted that largely, as far as education is concerned, in the direction of "giving our children a better chance than we had." This often meant giving our children the sort of education the landed aristocracy has had for centuries—or at least as much of that as possible. And too often that type of education, particularly as interpreted in popular educational demands, has been totally unsuited to present-day needs or to individual capacities and interests. Whenever this is the case, the emotional development of the pupil suffers.

Every teacher will encounter this influence many times even in his present career. There is supposedly more "class" to academic, collegiate education than to manual training and agriculture! Businessmen all too frequently regard "matriculation" as an exclusive hallmark of education! There is a real need for leadership in educating public opinion as to what education and the schools should stand for; and no teacher can get very far in any community without participating in and giving leadership to such public education.

The Rise of Industrialism. In some such manner as described above, schools for the general public were born and grew apace. As industry, the voice of the people, and other like influences acted as stimuli for increasing our educational facilities, conflicting interests and motives were bound to be reflected in our school program. The rapidity of democratic change, showing itself in education—especially since it followed a long period during which the relatively static educational perpetuation of class distinctions were characteristic—contributed to a sense of direct action. We felt we knew where we were going. Democracy, largely industrial and commercial in form, seemed to have come to stay. Children in school should be prepared for life—for life in such a social setting, where plenty of work, varied in kind, existed for all. Side by side with the old classical education—which has maintained its enormous momentum to a surprising degree—education as skills, bonds, things to be learned, played its powerful part. Each side—the classical and the utilitarian—competed with the other and formed to some extent a corrective for the other. But in this debate, worked out as one of the major compromises in our school system, the natural emphasis or form of competition was that of content. Should Latin, for example, be taught, or should we give more time to mechanical drawing, mathematics, and the like? Was education to be cultural, or useful? (As if these were different goals!)

This is important to us here. Where, under such consideration, does the child fit in? Are we teaching him certain *things,* such as the classics or mathematics, or are we teaching *him?*

The Cultural and the Useful. We shall return to this in a moment. But let us first proceed with our story. The attitude of debate between the cultural and the useful led to many familiar attempts at arguing one way or the other. Was there transfer of training? Did the classics give you *something* that carried over to other activities, apart from the classical knowledge which was soon largely forgotten on leaving school? Educational research was just springing up at this time; however, any naïve experiment could not fail to prove that however much Latin one learned, one did not thereby acquire a knowledge of astronomy or chemistry or French—unless, in the teaching of Latin, some overlap with these other fields was unwittingly included. Arguments counter to those based on such experiments pointed to life illustrations. After all, so many "great" people who had made outstanding contributions to society were classical scholars. Of course, classical education was "selective"; any intricate and difficult discipline demands outstanding ability for success. So that the old classical tradition was not killed outright by the ardent attacks upon it of our institutions for educational research. The budding Ph.D.'s could not convince the opposition entirely. And the man on the street, who had some power in electing trustees and representatives in the government, still kept demanding to some extent the supposedly more refined content of ancient and classical lore.

Because such a debate tended to sidetrack the educational issue into "should *this* or *that* be taught," the curriculum, even in its compromises, tended to consider factors other than child nature and its needs. Strange as it may seem, the defense of the academic and classical turned on the "usefulness" of such education, just as did the arguments used by the proponents of a thoroughly realistic education looking forward to the things a child would need to know or do when he left school. That being the case, education rapidly became a matter of organizing content that would be suited to needs *after* school days were over. The more varied industry became, the more varied our programs. Give a child a certain sample repertoire of facts and skills and send him out to make good. The opportunity is there. If he fails, it is his own fault, and not that of the school. Perhaps the church will take care of the failures—by converting them into humble and contrite citizens. If not, there are always the law courts and penal institutions as a line of last and invulnerable defense, behind which society stands secure from the dangers of the maladjusted or antisocial misfit. Or again, if not the jails, then the mental hospitals can house those who, though antisocial in a sense, are not in their right minds and therefore are not to be held responsible for their actions.

Perhaps the above statement is somewhat extreme in part. But in general it can be justified by any thorough analysis of our educational system prior to the recent interest in child *development*. We may add that such references as those made above to the church, legal institutions, industry, and so on are not to be interpreted as belittling religion, law, and the like. Rather the point of view is that as education becomes degraded into a squabble over content, so the true and unquestionable values even of religion are degraded. And this is always the case when the essential needs and satisfactions of the developing human being are overlooked, when the tried and proven human values are neglected in our considerations.

The Question of Special Aptitudes. There is yet more to the story, even in outline form such as we are using here. If education comes to be considered exclusively in terms of training for life after school, giving the pupil the right skills so that he may fit into a workaday world and make a living, many results are immediately evident. The brighter people can learn more facts and skills than the less bright. Out in society this will give them a better chance. Their advancement can be more rapid. Individualism, demanding freedom of individual action to as great a degree as possible, leads to the sort of competitive society that we are familiar with, particularly when we look at society with its great weaknesses, from a humanitarian point of view. Perhaps, too, there are special skills, demanded in the world outside the school, that only a few can acquire. Hence the familiar question of educational psychology—"Are there special inborn aptitudes?" Could we economize time in our educational system by analyzing human capacities to a very fine degree, and train children along narrow lines to fit them for the type of specialized niche that seems indicated by our psychological-test analysis? Vocational guidance, conceived in this form, burst forth in our training institutions and was fostered and encouraged by the industrialist. It was contributed to, also, by the fact that as the age range of compulsory school attendance was extended at the upper end, we soon found that to keep some children interested until the adolescent years required something more than the time-honored academic program. Education itself became more varied, particularly in its upper reaches.

The days—not more than fifteen or twenty years ago— of the rapid multiplication of special aptitude tests, are evidenced in all this. Luckily for education, their success has been very largely tempered by a high proportion of glorious failure, even though, out of the wreckage, a modicum of useful, psychologically sound progress has been achieved.[1] But here we would note in passing that undue outside influence in education, evidenced by such a movement as the analysis of human nature into capacities likely to be developed for the benefit of a narrowly conceived competitive industrialism, is something to be watched with considerable caution.

"Progressive Education." Against so narrow a conception of education, the "progressivists" made a staunch protest. The rights of the child to self-development, self-realization, freedom of action, freedom to develop his own potentialities, and so on, were the keynotes. An education was demanded, not for the benefit of an out-of-date, logically incompatible and inhuman competitive individualism, but for the benefit of the rising generation, the children themselves. In essence this has always been the emphasis of educational reformers through the ages— such men as Rousseau, Pestalozzi, Herbert, Froebel, Dewey. Because of the difficulties of working within the public system, the progressive-education movement tended to center itself in private schools. This has certain advantages, but many disadvantages. On the positive side, it gives greater freedom of action to the educator.

[1] See Chapter XI.

It enables him to try out certain procedures with smaller groups first, before launching into the chaos of untried technique with large numbers of children and with limited staffs. On the negative side, unless it is linked definitely with the public system, at least through some liaison officers, it sets itself up as something apart, critical of and criticized by the ordinary system. It also permits the fanatic and the faddist to work alone, without the benefit and salutary influence of general common-sense criticism.

This extremism, and the misguided efforts of the fanatic, who is himself often compensating by his radicalism for some unsolved personal conflict, have been the greatest weaknesses of the so-called Progressive Movement. When linked with sound inquiry and well-balanced educational outlook, it has performed great services to public education. But if based on an extremist view of human nature, it is just as unscientific and dangerous as any crass reactionary movement.

But public education and progressive education have recently come together more closely than ever before. While social progress and prosperity seemed readily definable, the function of the school in relation to society seemed clear. But with the recent throwing of all social shibboleths into the melting pot, with different countries advocating widely different solutions to our economic and social ills, the future fabric of the social order cannot be so clearly depicted. What is education to do? It cannot accept merely the slogan of training people for life in a defined social system. It must perforce revert to the emphasis on fostering sound mental outlook, equipping the child to participate constructively in social progress and human living, giving him a chance to contribute to the better conception of society that he must help to formulate. All the human values find a place in such commonly met expressions as "developing a sense of security," "fostering a sound mind in a sound body," "training for social participation and good citizenship," "assisting the individual towards self-realization at all times and to the fullest possible extent."

Fostering Child Development. What does this mean? It means, among other things, that the school is just another agency, participating with the home, the church, our social institutions generally, in directing healthy and worth-while development. Instead of regarding the home as responsible for teaching the child some things, the church other things, and the school still others, *all* institutions are directing the development of the child. Each institution may have its special facilities and ways and means, its own special subject matter, to a degree. But the differences among them sink into insignificance when compared with the main task of directing the development of the child.

It also means that the school, with its specialists (the teachers) in this matter of child development, must give leadership to the co-operative endeavors of the various social institutions. It should be able to do this in that it can, by its practices, stimulate widespread interest in child nature and human needs. It has been responsible for analyzing the best that is known or that has been suggested in this field. It can best dispel the false notions of those who regard the child's development in terms of learning *this* at home, learning *that* in school, and learning *the other* at Sunday school, and so on. This latter pattern of thought seldom leads to co-operation. More often it leads to relative isolation of the social responsibilities of the institutions concerned, the main reason for their coming together then being to criticize the weaknesses of one another. The teacher must realize his responsibility in this matter of educating the public as to the better modes of looking at and attacking educational problems.

It means, too, that the school's task is somewhat more readily definable than that of the other social institutions. Primarily, that task depends upon the understanding of the nature of human development and its needs. This understanding comes from two great sources: (1) a knowledge of the past, the crystallizations and achievements, successes and failures represented by race experience; and (2) a knowledge of the psychological nature of the child, of the desired outcomes in regard to mature personality, of the means by which the raw material can be directed in its development towards the desired outcome. We shall now consider these two sources in turn.

Appreciation of Race Experience. An appreciation of what race experience counts for and contains is necessary for several reasons. If one can speak legitimately of the "rights" of each new generation, the main "right" involves the transmission of the social heritage. That is what the progress of civilization necessarily implies and involves. Obviously, the details of race experience as it has accumulated through the ages cannot be transmitted. Education has the special functions, therefore, of selecting those aspects that mean most to the succeeding generation and transmitting them by short-cut methods. (We would emphasize the necessity for short-cut methods in that those who stress "learning by doing" exclusively often fail to capitalize on the advantages of sound pedagogical function. It took centuries for the modern conception of number to evolve; but the child can gain a very enriched appreciation of that conception in a short time. Calculus was a late outcome of race experience, yet can be taught to a university student in a few months.) This short-cut, selective transmission makes possible not only the equipping of the child to take his place in an adult world, where he must earn a living, but also the continued progress of race experience, since the new generation is able to build upon the best that has gone before, to obtain new human insight, to carry intellectual achievement further. The selective function enables the educator to capitalize on and push forward those pre-eminently satisfying forms of human endeavor that have proved themselves to be significant human values—science, art, philosophy, political, social, and economic values, religion, and the like.

This sounds like an essentially intellectualistic form of development; and, of course, development is dependent upon learning, and learning involves intellectual achievement. In that sense the task of the school may be legitimately regarded as fostering and directing intellectual development. It involves giving the child a chance to appreciate these values—all of them—and to enrich his appreciation of them in his everyday life. Some children will go farther in their appreciation of one than of the others; other children will differ in the values most satisfying to them. But all values will find some place in every individual's experience. It involves further the recognition of the fact that unless emotional development keeps pace with the intellectual, the individual's appreciation of what we are teaching will suffer. While the teacher cannot be expected to be a thorough-going clinical psychiatrist, he must, in his own interest, be on the lookout for and able to recognize emotional factors inhibiting the child's intellectual progress; and he must avoid as far as possible contributing to the development of those unfortunate factors. In this sense the school's task may be frankly recognized as being intellectualistic in form, particularly since any change in emotional outlook can itself be overcome only by further intelligent appreciation of life situations on the part of the child.

Understanding the Child. A knowledge of the psychological nature of the child, of desirable personality, of means of achieving the desired end—the second source of the teacher's understanding, mentioned above—has especially been the theme of the present Manual. Some of the questions to be asked by the teacher concerning every child under his direction are the following:

What is the potentiality represented by this child? How intelligent (educable) is he? What am I trying to teach him? Why? In his learning of this or of that, what change is taking place in him? What general values and generalized habits are being fostered, quite apart from the nature of the specific thing learned? How can this subject be presented so as to achieve a maximum degree of development in a worth-while direction? What is a worth-while direction for all children, and for this child in particular? What sort of boys and girls are graduating from my class or school? What, in my judgment, does "getting an education" mean? What, really, am I doing for the development of the boys and girls I teach, and what sort of development is it? Here, for example, is Jim, a dull-normal boy in Grade Eight. At sixteen, by repeating grades and by constant pressure and ceaseless driving, he is at last nearing his high-school entrance. But he hates school, he is oversensitive, lacking in self-confidence, and yet boastful, a bully, domineering and boisterous. He has been in juvenile court for stealing a bicycle. What has been my objective for Jim? Was it a sound objective? Is this what I want to do in my job as a teacher?

Questions of this sort can really be classified under the headings: (*a*) What do we wish the child to become? (*b*) What does he represent as a set of human material at the disposal of the educator? (*c*) What methods, situations, and subject matter may be used to produce from the given human material the desired product? To these questions every teacher must address himself continually, if the school is to play an adequate role in development, the role for which it primarily exists.

II. THE SCHOOLS OF TOMORROW

As a concluding section to this Manual, it is perhaps fitting to venture a few remarks about the *ideal school* —the school of the future. Keeping in mind the fact that the partnership between mental hygiene and education will become increasingly effective, the following descriptive comments are advanced under appropriate headings:

(*a*) *Philosophy*. There will be a constant awareness and clarification of the philosophy underlying school practices and organization. No stated set of formulas will ever serve to direct educational procedure. Education will become completely self-conscious, so that its activities will be constantly scrutinized from the point of view of how well they meet the fundamental needs of the pupils.

(*b*) *Administration*. The administration will cease to think *primarily* of rules, regulations, buildings, and economic management, and will become more conscious at all times of educational objectives. Orderly arrangement and management will be assumed as a matter of course, without placing undue emphasis on or making a fetish of rules and regulations. School buildings, for instance, will be bright, attractive, cheerful, and healthy places. Granted the minimum requirements of light, heat, humidity, ventilation, and space, the cheerfulness and attractiveness will be provided by the children themselves. Thus, the attention of the administration will become focused on those influences which promote sound, healthy development. Basic to this point of view will be the function of the school superintendent, who will provide leadership to board officials and teachers alike.

(c) *Professional training and selection.* Recognition of the importance of the teacher's personality, of his mature, cultural, scientific, progressive outlook, of his interest in, and understanding of, human nature and its needs, will lead to an increasing care in matters of training and selecting educational personnel. Knowledge of subject matter and skill in pedagogy will always have their place in these considerations; but, above all, insight into child development, and ability to maintain a healthful emotional atmosphere in the school community at all times, will become much more dominant than is the case as yet.

(d) *Curriculum.* The curriculum will be flexible, constantly enriched, and always geared to the needs of those for whom it exists—the pupils. Emotional growth and social understandings will be more adequately provided for than is the case when curricular content is determined largely by tradition. Ample opportunity will be provided for creative arts and the more human means of intercommunication and expression, as well as for the logical abstractions emphasized by the formalist.

(e) *Classroom activities and organization.* Classroom activities will be characterized by spontaneity, directed by the needs of individual pupils and of the social group. Whatever special arrangements in organization have to be made because of individual differences of capacity and experience, the constant aim of the teacher will be to set the educational stage so as to foster a maximum of intellectual challenge, interested activity, and social contribution, with a satisfying sense of progressive understanding and responsibility.

(*f*) *Community relationships.* The relationship between school and community will be one of harmonious and intelligent co-operation. This applies to the meaningfulness and purpose of the curriculum, the utilization of all social welfare and mental-hygiene agencies, home and school partnership, guidance and counseling, and the place of the teacher as a social leader.

(*g*) *Discipline.* In all matters of discipline, truancy, asocial or antisocial behavior, the attitude will be one of recognizing the needs of the child and furnishing the requisite educational opportunities. Possible difficulties will be anticipated increasingly as our mental-hygiene knowledge increases.

(*h*) *Human engineering.* The importance of the school as one of the great character-building agencies cannot be overestimated. Leadership in educational thought and practice will come from the school itself. The school will know its pupils as individuals: their needs, aspirations, potentialities, achievements, strengths, and weaknesses. And for its increasing understanding of the essential nature of development, the possibilities of enriched adulthood will be made increasingly clear.